Steck-Vaughn

Language Exercises

Book 8

Harcourt Achieve

Rigby · Saxon · Steck-Vaughn

www.HarcourtAchieve.com
1.800.531.5015

Acknowledgments

Macmillan/McGraw-Hill School Publishing Company: Pronunciation Key, reprinted with permission of the publisher, from *Macmillan School Dictionary 1*. Copyright © 1990 Macmillan Publishing Company, a division of Macmillan, Inc.

LANGUAGE EXERCISES Series:		
Book 1	Book 4	Book 7
Book 2	Book 5	Book 8
Book 3	Book 6	Review

ISBN 13: 978-1-4190-1876-3

ISBN 10: 1-4190-1876-0

6 7 8 0982 12 11

4500295074

Table of Contents

Check What You Know 1
Check What You Know Correlation Chart................4

Unit 1 Vocabulary

1 ▪ Synonyms and Antonyms 5
2 ▪ Homonyms...6
3 ▪ Homographs 7
4 ▪ Prefixes 8
5 ▪ Suffixes 9
6 ▪ Contractions 10
7 ▪ Compound Words 11
8 ▪ Connotation/Denotation 12
9 ▪ Idioms 13
Review 14
Using What You've Learned 16

Unit 2 Sentences

10 ▪ Recognizing Sentences 18
11 ▪ Types of Sentences....................................19
12 ▪ Complete Subjects and Predicates.............20
13 ▪ Simple Subjects and Predicates 21
14 ▪ Position of Subjects 22
15 ▪ Compound Subjects and Predicates............23
16 ▪ Combining Sentences.................................24
17 ▪ Direct Objects 25
18 ▪ Indirect Objects 26
19 ▪ Independent and Subordinate Clauses.............27
20 ▪ Adjective and Adverb Clauses 28
21 ▪ Compound and Complex Sentences 29
22 ▪ Correcting Run-on Sentences.....................31
23 ▪ Expanding Sentences 32
Review 33
Using What You've Learned 35

Unit 3 Grammar and Usage

24 ▪ Common and Proper Nouns 37
25 ▪ Concrete, Abstract, and Collective Nouns 38
26 ▪ Singular and Plural Nouns 39
27 ▪ Possessive Nouns 41
28 ▪ Appositives...42
29 ▪ Verbs..43
30 ▪ Verb Phrases 44

31 ▪ Verb Tenses 45
32 ▪ Using Irregular Verbs 46
33 ▪ Mood 51
34 ▪ Transitive and Intransitive Verbs 52
35 ▪ Active and Passive Voice 54
36 ▪ Gerunds 55
37 ▪ Infinitives..56
38 ▪ Participles 57
39 ▪ Using Lie/Lay 58
40 ▪ Using Sit/Set and Learn/Teach 59
41 ▪ Pronouns..60
42 ▪ Using Its and It's 61
43 ▪ Demonstrative and Indefinite Pronouns.............62
44 ▪ Antecedents 63
45 ▪ Relative Pronouns.......................................64
46 ▪ Using Who/Whom 65
47 ▪ Using Pronouns 66
48 ▪ Adjectives...67
49 ▪ Demonstrative Adjectives 69
50 ▪ Comparing with Adjectives..........................70
51 ▪ Adverbs 71
52 ▪ Comparing with Adverbs.............................72
53 ▪ Using Adjectives and Adverbs 73
54 ▪ Prepositions and Prepositional Phrases 74
55 ▪ Conjunctions 76
56 ▪ Double Negatives..77
Review 78
Using What You've Learned 80

Unit 4 Capitalization and Punctuation

57 ▪ Using Capital Letters...................................82
58 ▪ Using End Punctuation 84
59 ▪ Using Commas 86
60 ▪ Using Quotation Marks and Apostrophes 88
61 ▪ Using Colons and Semicolons 89
62 ▪ Using Other Punctuation 90
Review 91
Using What You've Learned 93

Unit 5 Composition

63 ▪ Writing Sentences.......................................95
64 ▪ Writing Paragraphs 96
65 ▪ Writing Topic Sentences 97
66 ▪ Writing Supporting Details 98
67 ▪ Topic and Audience.....................................99

68 ▪ Brainstorming....................................100
69 ▪ Outlining...101
70 ▪ Persuasive Composition 102
71 ▪ Revising and Proofreading................104
Review 106
Using What You've Learned 108

85 ▪ Using an Almanac............................124
86 ▪ Choosing Reference Sources 125
87 ▪ Using Reference Sources 126
Review 128
Using What You've Learned 130

Unit 6 Study Skills

72 ▪ Dictionary: Syllables........................110
73 ▪ Dictionary: Pronunciation 111
74 ▪ Dictionary: Definitions and Parts of Speech....112
75 ▪ Dictionary: Etymologies...................113
76 ▪ Using Parts of a Book 114
77 ▪ Using Visual Aids 115
78 ▪ Using the Library 117
79 ▪ Using the Card Catalog....................118
80 ▪ Using an Encyclopedia.....................119
81 ▪ Using an Encyclopedia Index............120
82 ▪ Using a Thesaurus...........................121
83 ▪ Using the Readers' Guide.................122
84 ▪ Using an Atlas................................123

Final Reviews

Unit 1 132
Unit 2 134
Unit 3 136
Unit 4 138
Unit 5 140
Unit 6 142

Check What You've Learned 144
Check What You've Learned Correlation Chart 147

Answer Key..148

Index...Inside Back Cover

A. Write S before each pair of synonyms, A before each pair of antonyms, and H before each pair of homonyms.

1. _____ aloud, allowed

2. _____ tiny, miniature

3. _____ argumentative, agreeable

4. _____ massive, giant

B. Write the homograph for the pair of meanings.

1. **a.** to move slowly   **b.** a unit of measurement _____

C. Write P before each word with a prefix, S before each word with a suffix, and C before each compound word.

1. _____ wishful

2. _____ overblown

3. _____ unruly

4. _____ misinform

D. Write the words that make up each contraction.

1. they've _____ _____   2. we'll _____ _____

E. Underline the word in parentheses that has the more positive connotation.

The (generous, pushy) baker insisted we try the hot cookies.

F. Circle the letter of the idiom that means depressed.

1. **a.** down in the dumps   **b.** in the doghouse

G. Write D before the declarative sentence, IM before the imperative sentence, E before the exclamatory sentence, and IN before the interrogative sentence. Then underline the simple subject, and circle the simple predicate in each sentence.

1. _____ Look out for that hole!

2. _____ Please hand me the towel.

3. _____ Why are you still here?

4. _____ I usually leave at noon.

H. Write CS before the sentence that has a compound subject and CP before the sentence that has a compound predicate.

1. _____ Peaches and strawberries are great in pies.

2. _____ We watched and cheered our team.

I. Write CS before the compound sentence, RO before the run-on sentence, and I before the sentence that is in inverted order.

1. _____ You have a toothache, you should go to the dentist.

2. _____ I wanted chocolate, but they only had vanilla.

3. _____ Up the tree scampered the squirrel.

J. Put brackets ([ ]) around the subordinate clause, and underline the independent clause in this complex sentence. Then write DO above the direct object.

The doctor handed Jesse the prescription that he needed.

K. Underline the common nouns, and circle the proper nouns in the sentence.

Ms. Chang rounded up the group and began the tour of the Jefferson Memorial.

L. Circle the appositive in the sentence. Underline the noun it identifies or explains.

My favorite uncle, Tom Fiske, was recently elected mayor of Greenville.

M. Write past, present, or future to show the tense of each underlined verb.

1. _____ Kathy painted one wall in her kitchen pale blue.

2. _____ Peter will call tomorrow morning at eight o'clock.

3. _____ Each morning before breakfast, Juan walks two miles.

4. _____ I will go to the library today.

N. Circle the correct verbs in each sentence.

1. There (is, are) only six weeks left before we (go, went) on vacation.

2. Steve (set, sat) down and (lay, laid) the sleeping kitten in his lap.

3. To (teach, learn) how to ski, you should (take, took) lessons.

4. (Sit, Set) the plate beside the sink where the glasses are (sitting, setting).

O. Circle the number of the sentence that is in the active voice.

1. The packages were sent two weeks ago.

2. Phillip leaped to his feet to disagree with the speaker.

P. Write SP before the sentence that has a subject pronoun, OP before the sentence that has an object pronoun, PP before the sentence that has a possessive pronoun, and IP before the sentence that has an indefinite pronoun. Circle the pronoun in each sentence.

1. _____ Nobody understands what happened.

2. _____ Ellen played the first song for him.

3. _____ The horse raised its head to look at the dog.

4. _____ He sent the memo to four people.

Q. Underline the pronoun. Circle its antecedent.

Janet and Jason met to discuss the response to their request.

R. Write adjective or adverb to describe the underlined word.

1. _____ These days are the best of the summer.

2. _____ Charlotte tiptoed quietly past the open door.

3. _____ That was the most difficult skating move I've ever seen.

4. _____ I really like Canadian bacon on my pizza.

5. _____ The dachshund is a tiny breed of dog.

6. _____ That heavy tree will be extremely hard to move.

S. Underline each prepositional phrase twice. Circle each preposition. Underline the conjunction once.

I don't have the time or the patience to talk about the complaints of those people.

T. Rewrite the letter. Add capital letters and punctuation where needed.

591 w franklin place
bent tree tx 78709
jan 27 2006

dear ms coleman

please know that I called you at exactly 915 but nobody answered the phone ___ i hope that youll allow me another opportunity to tell you about my work ___ i have exciting news ___ i won the national photo contest and my picture will be in the next issue of parks of the world ___

i look forward to speaking with you ___ please call anytime this week between 1000 and 230 ___ ill be in one of these places my home my office or my car you have all three numbers ___

sincerely

eric flannery

_____

_____

_____

_____

_____

_____

_____

_____

_____

_____

_____

U. Number the sentences in order, with the topic sentence first.

1. _____ Then they walk to find water, and they drink their fill.

2. _____ An elephant herd walks and eats most of the day.

3. _____ The herd wakes early to graze before it gets too hot.

4. _____ Finally, they lie down and sleep.

V. Write brainstorming, outlining, or persuading to describe each of the following.

1. organizing your thoughts before you write _____

2. convincing others to accept a personal opinion _____

3. bringing to mind as many ideas as possible _____

W. Rewrite the sentence below. Correct the errors in the sentence by following the proofreader's marks.

As the movie began, crowd the grew silent and and consentraited on the actshun.

_____

X. Use the dictionary entry to answer the questions.

> **honor** (än'ər) *n.* **1.** esteem; respect. **2.** recognition. [Old French *honor*]

1. What part of speech is the word honor? _____

2. Would honest come before or after honor? _____

3. Which language is in the history of the word honor? _____

4. Write the word for this respelling: (sis' tem) _____

5. Write honor separated into syllables. _____

n.	noun
pron.	pronoun
v.	verb
adj.	adjective
adv.	adverb
prep.	preposition

Y. Write the letter of the reference source in the blank before its description.

_____ 1. used to find synonyms and antonyms   **a.** dictionary

_____ 2. a visual aid that lists information in rows and columns   **b.** card catalog

_____ 3. lists articles in magazines by author and subject   **c.** encyclopedia

_____ 4. used to find definitions, pronunciations, and origins of words   **d.** chart

_____ 5. presents information about geographical locations   **e.** atlas

_____ 6. contains specific yearly information on a variety of topics   **f.** *Readers' Guide*

_____ 7. a source of articles about many different people and things   **g.** almanac

_____ 8. contains information cards on every book in the library   **h.** thesaurus

---

Below is a list of the sections on *Check What You Know* and the pages on which the skills in each section are taught. If you missed any questions, turn to the pages listed, and practice the skills. Then correct the problems you missed on *Check What You Know.*

Section	Practice Page	Section	Practice Page	Section	Practice Page
Unit 1		J	25, 27–30	*Unit 4*	
A	5, 6	*Unit 3*		T	82–90
B	7	K	37		
C	8, 9, 11	L	42	*Unit 5*	
D	10	M	45	U	96–98
E	12	N	46–50, 58–59	V	100–103
F	13	O	54	W	104–105
Unit 2		P	60–62		
G	19, 21	Q	63, 66	*Unit 6*	
H	23	R	67–73	X	110–113
I	22, 29–31	S	74–76	Y	110–113, 115–127

Synonyms and Antonyms

> ■ A **synonym** is a word that has the same or nearly the same meaning as one or more other words. EXAMPLES: sick – ill   sad – unhappy

A. Write a synonym for each word below.

1. discover _____
2. ridiculous _____
3. difficult _____

4. weary _____
5. beautiful _____
6. inquire _____

7. capable _____
8. funny _____
9. honest _____

B. Rewrite the following sentences, using synonyms for the underlined words.

1. The vacant lot became the neighborhood playground.

   _____

2. His broken leg slowly began to mend.

   _____

3. The Barkers returned from their trip weary, but happy.

   _____

4. The energetic dog bounded across the lawn.

   _____

> ■ An **antonym** is a word that has the opposite meaning of another word.
> EXAMPLES: high – low   giant – tiny

C. Write an antonym for each word below.

1. graceful _____
2. difficult _____
3. generous _____

4. hastily _____
5. deflate _____
6. valuable _____

7. definite _____
8. superior _____
9. abundance _____

D. For each underlined word, underline the correct antonym.

1. Her failure was no surprise to those who knew her well.   (success, defeat)
2. Dr. Fenton always has a mean greeting for her patients.   (sarcastic, friendly)
3. His cowardly actions went unnoticed.   (courageous, fearful)
4. Our car is old and dependable.   (valuable, unreliable)
5. His vague answer cleared up the misunderstanding.   (rambling, specific)

> ■ A **homonym** is a word that sounds the same as another word but has a different spelling and a different meaning.
> EXAMPLES: their – they're – there   hear – here

A. Underline the correct homonym(s) in each sentence below.

1. What is the (weight, wait) of that rocket?

2. The (sale, sail) on the lake will be rough today.

3. Don't you like to (brows, browse) around in a bookstore?

4. We spent several (days, daze) at an old-fashioned (in, inn).

5. The ship was caught in an ice (flow, floe).

6. A large (boulder, bolder) rolled down the mountainside.

7. Why is that crowd on the (pier, peer)?

8. They asked the bank for a (lone, loan).

9. We drove four miles in a foggy (missed, mist).

10. Don't you like to (sea, see) a field of golden wheat?

11. Jack (threw, through) the ball (threw, through) the garage window.

12. We (buy, by) our fish from the market down on the (beach, beech).

13. The band will march down the middle (aisle, isle) of the auditorium.

14. Who is the (principal, principle) of your school?

15. The United States Congress (meats, meets) in the capitol in Washington, D.C.

16. The farmer caught the horse by the (rain, reign, rein).

17. She stepped on the (break, brake) suddenly.

18. (Their, There) are too many people to get on this boat.

19. The wren (flew, flue) in a (strait, straight) line.

20. We were not (allowed, aloud) to visit the museum yesterday.

B. Write a homonym for each word below.

1. weigh _____

2. steal _____

3. sail _____

4. fare _____

5. maid _____

6. deer _____

7. ate _____

8. vain _____

9. strait _____

10. threw _____

11. soar _____

12. bored _____

13. see _____

14. sent _____

15. pare _____

16. peace _____

17. sun _____

18. blue _____

■ A **homograph** is a word that has the same spelling as another word but a different meaning and sometimes a different pronunciation.
  EXAMPLE: <u>base</u>, meaning "the bottom on which a statue stands," and <u>base</u>, meaning "mean and selfish"

A. Write the homograph for each pair of meanings below.

1. **a.** a large animal   **b.** to support or carry   _____

2. **a.** a person that jumps   **b.** a type of dress   _____

3. **a.** a cutting tool   **b.** the past tense of <u>see</u> _____

4. **a.** to hit   **b.** a sweetened beverage   _____

5. **a.** to be silent   **b.** a type of flower   _____

6. **a.** a glass container   **b.** to rattle or shake   _____

7. **a.** a round object   **b.** a formal dance   _____

8. **a.** part of the eye   **b.** a student   _____

B. Fill in each blank with a homograph from the box.

ball	punch	bear	jar
jumper	mum	saw	pupil

1. Jim and I _____ that movie last week.

2. The pitcher threw the _____ to home plate.

3. Joan's new _____ fit her very well.

4. Sharpen that _____ before you cut the wood.

5. That yellow _____ is the prettiest flower in the vase.

6. Jerry made a delicious _____ for the party.

7. The _____ was filled with strawberry jam.

8. The new _____ made new friends in school.

9. That _____ had two cubs yesterday.

10. My parents attended a formal _____ in Boston, Massachusetts.

Lesson 4 — Prefixes

> ■ A **prefix** added to the beginning of a base word changes the meaning of the word.
>
>   EXAMPLE: in-, meaning "not," + the base word <u>visible</u> = <u>invisible</u>, meaning "not visible"
>
> | EXAMPLES: | prefix | meaning | prefix | meaning |
> |---|---|---|---|---|
> | | in- | not | re- | again |
> | | dis- | not | fore- | before |
> | | un- | not | mis- | wrong |
> | | im- | not | co- | together |
> | | il- | not, non | pre- | before |

A. On the blank after each sentence, write a new word that means the same as the two underlined words combined. Use prefixes from the examples above. Use a dictionary if needed.

1. Susan was asked to <u>write</u> her report <u>again</u>. _____

2. At first, Susan was <u>not pleased</u> with the idea. _____

3. Then she remembered that the instructor had <u>warned</u> the class <u>before</u> that

   handwriting must be neat. _____

4. Susan looked at her paper and realized that it was <u>not possible</u> to

   read some of the words. _____

5. "I am <u>not certain</u> myself what the last sentence says," she thought. _____

6. "Did I <u>spell</u> that word <u>wrong</u>?" she wondered. _____

7. Susan realized that she tended to be <u>not patient</u> about her work. _____

B. Add a prefix from the examples above to each word to make a new word. Then write the new word on the blank.

1. read _____

2. pure _____

3. wrap _____

4. understand _____

5. mature _____

6. arrange _____

7. equal _____

8. obey _____

9. match _____

10. view _____

11. locate _____

12. fortune _____

13. pay _____

14. fair _____

Lesson 5 — Suffixes

- A **suffix** added to the end of a base word changes the meaning of the word.
  EXAMPLE: -ward, meaning "toward," + the base word <u>west</u> = <u>westward</u>, meaning "toward the west"
- Sometimes you need to change the spelling of a base word when a suffix is added.
  EXAMPLE: imagine – imagination

EXAMPLES:	suffix	meaning	suffix	meaning
	-less	without	-en	to make
	-ish	of the nature of	-ist	one skilled in
	-ous	full of	-able	able to be
	-er	one who does	-tion	art of
	-hood	state of being	-ful	full of
	-ward	in the direction of	-al	pertaining to
	-ness	quality of	-ible	able to be
	-ment	act or process of	-like	similar to

A. Add a suffix from the examples above to each base word in parentheses. Write the new word in the sentence.

1. Kito wants to be a _____. (paint)

2. He is _____, working after school to earn money for art lessons. (tire)

3. People say that his portraits are very _____. (life)

4. His talent as an _____ was apparent at an early age. (art)

5. In kindergarten his teacher noticed his _____ understanding of shapes and forms. (remark)

6. She gave Kito a great deal of freedom and _____. (encourage)

7. Kito had a _____ for color. (fascinate)

8. Throughout his _____, he entered many contests and competitions. (child)

9. His friends expect that he will become a _____ artist. (fame)

B. Add a suffix from the examples above to each root word. Then write the new word on the blank.

1. rely _____

2. glory _____

3. color _____

4. occasion _____

5. fate _____

6. comfort _____

7. hope _____

8. believe _____

- A **contraction** is a word formed by joining two other words.
- An **apostrophe** shows where a letter or letters have been left out.
  EXAMPLE: he would = he'd
- Won't is an exception.
  EXAMPLE: will not = won't

A. Write a sentence in which you use a contraction for each pair of words below.

1. I am _____

2. is not _____

3. do not _____

4. where is _____

5. should not _____

6. was not _____

7. were not _____

8. we will _____

9. they are _____

10. I have _____

B. Underline the contractions in the sentences below. Then write the two words that make up each contraction.

1. John and Janet won't be home until dinnertime. _____

2. Let's surprise them by having dinner ready. _____

3. Yes, that's a great idea. _____

4. I don't know what to cook. _____

5. I think we'd better have spaghetti. _____

6. Yes, we can't fail with that. _____

7. It's John's favorite. _____

8. Besides, you're the best spaghetti cook in the family. _____

9. We'll have so much fun! _____

10. John doesn't know how lucky he is. _____

Lesson 7
Compound Words

- A **compound word** is a word that is made up of two or more words. The meaning of compound words is related to the meaning of each individual word.
  - EXAMPLE: sail + boat = sailboat, meaning "a boat that uses sails to move through water"
- Compound words may be written as one word, as hyphenated words, or as separate words.
  - EXAMPLES: airport   air-condition   air force

A. Combine the words in the list to make compound words. You may use words more than once.

sand	fall	paper	color	home	water	room	play
made	field	under	come	out	stand	mate	back

1. _____
2. _____
3. _____
4. _____
5. _____
6. _____

7. _____
8. _____
9. _____
10. _____
11. _____
12. _____

B. Answer the following questions.

1. The word <u>books</u> sometimes refers to "financial accounts."

   What is a <u>bookkeeper</u>? _____

2. A <u>fast</u> is "a period of time when a person eats little or nothing."

   What does <u>breakfast</u> actually mean? _____

3. <u>Ferry</u> means "to transport across a body of water."

   What is a <u>ferryboat</u>? _____

4. A <u>lord</u> is "a person who has great authority over something."

   What is a <u>landlord</u>? _____

5. <u>Jelly</u> is "a soft, transparent substance." What is a <u>jellyfish</u>?

   _____

6. Since <u>out</u> means "outside of," what is an <u>outlaw</u>?

   _____

■ The **denotation** of a word is its exact meaning as stated in a dictionary.
  EXAMPLE: The denotation of casual is "not fancy or formal."
■ The **connotation** of a word is an added meaning that suggests
  something positive or negative.
  EXAMPLES: **Negative:** Sloppy suggests "very messy." Sloppy has a
  negative connotation.
  Positive: Casual suggests "informal or relaxed." Casual
  has a positive connotation.
■ Some words are neutral. They do not suggest either good or bad feelings.
  EXAMPLES: calendar, toy, pencil

A. Write (–) if the word has a negative connotation. Write (+) if it has a positive connotation. Write (N) if the word is neutral.

1. _____ lazy	5. _____ pretty	9. _____ make
_____ relaxed	_____ gorgeous	_____ create
2. _____ determined	6. _____ grand	10. _____ weird
_____ stubborn	_____ large	_____ unique
3. _____ drug	7. _____ old	11. _____ criticize
_____ remedy	_____ antique	_____ evaluate
4. _____ clever	8. _____ curious	12. _____ snooty
_____ sneaky	_____ nosy	_____ refined

B. Rewrite the paragraph below. Replace the underlined words with words that do not have a negative connotation.

Jason shoved his way through the mob of people. He swaggered through the doorway and slouched against the wall. His clothes were quite gaudy. He glared at everyone with hostile eyes. Then he snickered and said in a loud tone, "I'm finally here."

_____

_____

_____

_____

_____

_____

_____

> ■ An **idiom** is an expression that has a meaning different from the usual meanings of the individual words within it.
>
> EXAMPLE: We're all in the same boat means "We're in a similar situation," not, "We're all in a watercraft together."

A. Read each sentence. Then write the letter of the corresponding idiom for the underlined word or words.

A. shaken up	**D.** beside herself	**G.** comes through	**J.** down in the dumps
B. fly off the handle	**E.** in a bind	**H.** in the doghouse	**K.** stands up for
C. on cloud nine	**F.** put up with	**I.** on the fence	

1. One day Julia will be <u>sad</u>. _____

2. The next day you may find her <u>unbelievably happy</u>. _____

3. But be careful when Julia is <u>very scared or confused</u>. _____

4. She's liable to <u>become suddenly angry</u>. _____

5. Julia always <u>defends</u> her views, no matter what. _____

6. She won't <u>allow</u> any argument. _____

7. One time when I insisted that she listen to my viewpoint, she was <u>really upset</u>. _____

8. I was <u>out of favor</u> for weeks. _____

9. On the other hand, when a friend of Julia's is <u>in a difficult situation</u>, she really <u>helps</u>. _____ _____

10. Like a true friend, Julia is there when I am <u>unable to make a decision</u>. _____

B. For the underlined idiom in each sentence below, write the usual meaning of the words that make up the idiom.

1. Kelly can't decide whether she wants to go, so our plans are still <u>up in the air</u>. _____undecided_____

2. If I get the job, I'll be <u>walking on air</u>. _____

3. My friend's business is <u>on the skids</u>. _____

4. George's ideas are <u>off the wall</u>. _____

5. That's enough silliness. Let's <u>talk turkey</u>. _____

6. Victor was <u>in hot water</u> for not cleaning the garage. _____

7. The audience was <u>all ears</u> when you spoke. _____

8. The lost book <u>turned up</u> yesterday. _____

9. Jan and I <u>put our heads together</u> to solve the problem. _____

A. Write S before each pair of synonyms. Write A before each pair of antonyms. Write H before each pair of homonyms.

1. _____ study, consider
2. _____ expand, reduce
3. _____ attempt, endeavor
4. _____ away, aweigh
5. _____ grouchy, pleasant
6. _____ move, budge
7. _____ arc, ark
8. _____ response, reply
9. _____ bolder, boulder
10. _____ stride, walk
11. _____ doubting, trustful
12. _____ boy, buoy
13. _____ frolic, romp
14. _____ panicky, poised
15. _____ chilly, chili
16. _____ hangar, hanger
17. _____ shout, yell
18. _____ site, sight
19. _____ civilized, primitive
20. _____ kind, humane
21. _____ stable, changeable
22. _____ compliment, complement
23. _____ simple, difficult
24. _____ outspoken, shy

B. In each sentence below, circle the correct definition for the underlined homograph.

1. Once a month I get a yen to go out for a nice dinner.
   a. a unit of money in Japan   b. strong desire
2. My favorite cereal has nuts, dates, and raisins.
   a. sweet, dark fruits   b. days, months, and years
3. The batter swung at the pitch but missed the ball.
   a. a baseball player   b. a liquid mixture for baking
4. Our choices of dessert included fresh cobbler with ice cream.
   a. a mender of shoes   b. a fruit pie with one crust

C. Underline each word that has a prefix. Write its meaning on the line.

1. movie preview _____
2. nonprofit organization _____
3. unusual design _____
4. mistaken identity _____

D. Underline each word that has a suffix. Write its meaning on the line.

1. thoughtless person _____
2. unreadable writing _____
3. unbeatable price _____
4. dangerous curve _____

E. In each sentence, underline the words that could form contractions. Then write the contractions on the lines.

1. It is time for the summer festival at the lake. _____

2. I wonder what is taking them so long. _____

3. You have had enough time to answer that. _____

4. If you won, it would be the happiest day of your life. _____

5. Jessica should not be so impatient with her friends. _____

6. I would like to go with you. _____

F. Underline the compound word in each sentence. Then write its definition on the line.

1. The gash in her forehead needed sixteen stitches. _____

2. Everything you heard is absolutely true. _____

3. Get a Sunday paper at the nearest newsstand. _____

4. My roommate never remembers to water the plants. _____

5. The underwater world is fascinating. _____

6. I buy groceries at the supermarket on the corner. _____

G. Answer the following questions.

1. Would you rather be considered smart or brilliant? _____

2. Would you prefer a helpful or an interfering neighbor? _____

3. Which is more admirable, being thrifty or cheap? _____

4. Which is less polite, to sip a drink or to gulp it? _____

5. Would you rather be considered clumsy or graceful? _____

H. Underline the idiom in each sentence. On the line after each sentence, explain what the idiom means.

1. Sometimes it's hard to make ends meet. _____

2. Jeff's turning over a new leaf now. _____

3. Trying to fool her is skating on thin ice. _____

4. We ran into our old friend at the shopping mall. _____

5. I was all ears when she told me the news. _____

A. Read each sentence. Then combine the base word below the blank and a prefix or suffix from the box to form another word. Write the new word in the blank. You may have to make changes in spelling.

re-	fore-	-ist	-able	-ous	-al	im-	-ful

1. My new desk is a _____ example of French woodworking artistry.
   marvel

2. When our first plan didn't work, we had to _____ our strategy.
   think

3. Her response was a _____ denial of the charges.
   force

4. The Russian _____ astounded the audience with his skill.
   piano

5. Our car has an _____ steering wheel.
   adjust

6. Cleaning the garage before noon seemed an _____ task.
   possible

7. In the second race, Greg moved to the _____ of the competition.
   front

8. She wrote a _____ note to the author of the book she loved.
   person

B. Underline the word that has a positive connotation in each pair.

1. A (group, gang) of employees planned a meeting.

2. The man (walked, stomped) into the room.

3. José (asked, demanded) to see the manager.

4. The (puny, fragile) vase was very old.

5. Do you smell a pleasant (fragrance, odor)?

6. David made a (tasty, bland) stew for dinner.

7. The biscuits were baked to a (golden, dark) brown.

8. The (confident, arrogant) young man spoke at the convention.

9. Dan (wrote, scribbled) a note to his grandmother.

10. The (soiled, filthy) clothes needed to be washed.

11. The boy (leaned, slouched) against the doorway.

12. The (reckless, brave) firefighter entered the burning building.

C. In each pair of sentences below, put a check before the one that contains an idiom.

1. _____ "Keep your chin up. Things aren't as bad as they seem," Joe said.

   _____ "Please keep your chin up while I button the top button," Jill said.

2. _____ Sue was mad at her friend and gave her the cold shoulder.

   _____ Cynthia took the cold shoulder of beef out of the refrigerator.

3. _____ It seemed that the clock slowly ticked off the minutes until lunchtime.

   _____ Beth was ticked off when her friend didn't return her call.

4. _____ Watching clock hands move is for the birds.

   _____ This bag of seed is for the birds.

5. _____ "I've been on a merry-go-round all week," Nancy exclaimed.

   _____ "Mom, we went on a merry-go-round at the carnival!" Jody exclaimed.

6. _____ Jean's problem was so confusing that she was all at sea.

   _____ The sailors were all at sea when the storm began.

7. _____ We often take a walk through the woods to see the wildflowers.

   _____ Craig tells his little sister to take a walk whenever she bothers him.

8. _____ The action of the movie picked up during the second half.

   _____ Joe picked up his clothes and put them away.

D. Put a check before the definition of each underlined idiom.

1. John has a bad temper and flies off the handle at the smallest thing.

   _____ leaps from a wagon

   _____ is easily angered

   _____ soars over a frying pan

2. "Try to keep out of hot water," José told his little brother.

   _____ stay clear of the stove

   _____ take a cold shower

   _____ avoid trouble

3. "You can bank on Juan to keep his promises," Mary said.

   _____ build on

   _____ depend on

   _____ deposit money

4. Ryan kept his head when the fire started, and he called for help.

   _____ didn't let his head fall off

   _____ didn't talk suddenly

   _____ didn't panic

5. Stand up for your rights, and don't let people walk all over you.

   _____ trample you on the ground

   _____ take advantage of you

   _____ step on your feet

6. "I take what Kelly says with a grain of salt," Sarah said.

   _____ very lightly

   _____ by eating a little salt

   _____ seriously

7. Joe refused to swallow the line that Jason gave him.

   _____ drink something

   _____ eat the fishing line

   _____ believe the words

8. Nina nearly jumped out of her skin at the movie about ghosts.

   _____ removed her skin

   _____ was startled and frightened

   _____ split her skin open

> ■ A **sentence** is a group of words that expresses a complete thought.
> EXAMPLE: He has not worked since he injured his leg.

■ **Some of the following groups of words are sentences, and some are not. Write S**
before each group that is a sentence. Punctuate each sentence with a period.

_____ 1. In planning our work schedule____

_____ 2. December is the last month of the year____

_____ 3. Last year when it snowed for eight days____

_____ 4. Another way to improve the quality of your voice____

_____ 5. The largest city in Illinois is Chicago____

_____ 6. There is no way to know what will happen____

_____ 7. Enter the house very quietly____

_____ 8. On one of our hikes in the park____

_____ 9. Houston is the largest gulf port____

_____ 10. An outstanding quarterback with the ability to throw long passes____

_____ 11. Paul Revere was a silversmith____

_____ 12. Check all your sentences carefully____

_____ 13. High on a wooded hill, the cabin____

_____ 14. The cats had a wonderful time running among the bushes____

_____ 15. After wading a long distance in the stream____

_____ 16. As the hour approached for the program____

_____ 17. Kathleen has been learning to become a mechanic ____

_____ 18. Don't throw those papers away ____

_____ 19. California is the third largest state in the United States ____

_____ 20. There are many mountain streams in the Ozarks____

_____ 21. Before they reached the edge of the cliff____

_____ 22. Many notable Americans are buried in the National Cathedral____

_____ 23. In the early morning, the wind became cold____

_____ 24. The silvery airplane____

_____ 25. From the spaceship onto the carrier____

_____ 26. Here comes the delivery truck____

_____ 27. W. C. Handy is known as the "Father of the Blues"____

_____ 28. While on vacation in Florida____

_____ 29. Sometime tomorrow morning____

_____ 30. Laurie and I picked apples this morning____

Types of Sentences

> - A **declarative sentence** makes a statement. It is followed by a period (.).   EXAMPLE: Insects have six legs.
> - An **interrogative sentence** asks a question. It is followed by a question mark (?).   EXAMPLE: What are you eating?
> - An **imperative sentence** expresses a command or request. It is followed by a period (.).   EXAMPLE: Open the window.
> - An **exclamatory sentence** expresses strong emotion. It can also express a command or request that is made with great excitement. It is followed by an exclamation point (!).   EXAMPLES: The grass is on fire! Hurry over here!

■ Write **D** for declarative, **IN** for interrogative, **IM** for imperative, or **E** for exclamatory before each sentence. Put the correct punctuation at the end of each sentence.

_____   1. What do you consider a fair price____

_____   2. How many people signed a contract____

_____   3. Do not leave objects lying on floors and stairways____

_____   4. Mary Bethune became the first black woman to head a federal agency____

_____   5. What a cold day it is____

_____   6. Ryan, where have you been____

_____   7. Return those books when you have finished with them____

_____   8. I bought this scarf in Mexico____

_____   9. Look at that gorgeous sunset____

_____   10. Copy each problem accurately____

_____   11. Books are storehouses of knowledge____

_____   12. My pet snake is loose____

_____   13. How do forests help prevent floods____

_____   14. Where did we get the word September____

_____   15. Listen attentively____

_____   16. Rice is the most widely eaten food in the world____

_____   17. Don't lose the book____

_____   18. Paul's cousins from South Dakota will arrive Saturday____

_____   19. Did you buy more cereal____

_____   20. We saw the new tiger exhibit at the zoo____

_____   21. Put those books on that shelf____

_____   22. Do you want to help me make bread____

_____   23. We're out of flour____

_____   24. Wait for me____

_____   25. How old is that oak tree____

- Every sentence has two main parts, a **complete subject** and a **complete predicate.**
- The complete subject includes all the words that tell who or what the sentence is about.
  EXAMPLE: **The southern section of our state**/has many forests.
- The complete predicate includes all the words that state the action or condition of the subject.
  EXAMPLE: The southern section of our state/**has many forests.**

- **Draw a line between the complete subject and the complete predicate in each sentence below.**

1. An earthquake formed Reelfoot Lake in 1811.
2. The deepest places in the oceans are in the Mariana Trench in the Pacific.
3. The seasons are the four divisions of the year.
4. Many of the people waited instead of crowding into the bus.
5. The two mechanics have not yet fixed the car.
6. The first telegraph line was between Baltimore, Maryland, and Washington, D.C.
7. The territory of Iowa was formed from a part of the Louisiana Purchase.
8. The origin of the wheat plant is very obscure.
9. The television tube was a product of many years of experimentation.
10. The shortest day of the year is in December.
11. Workers discussed timely topics at the meeting.
12. Fossils show that ferns 100 feet high once grew in Kansas.
13. Great deposits of bauxite, from which aluminum is extracted, exist in Arkansas.
14. The Shoshone live in Wyoming, Idaho, and Nevada.
15. The citizens of Georgia built Fort Pulaski over one hundred years ago.
16. Who originated Father's Day?
17. Many people watched the airliner take off.
18. Mexican silver mines were worked before the Spanish conquest.
19. A steamboat was used on the Mississippi River for the first time in 1811.
20. Who brought in the mail?
21. Benjamin Franklin was once an apprentice to his brother.
22. All of the guests enjoyed the picnic.
23. Annapolis Academy was founded in 1845.
24. The three cities that we visited were New York, Montreal, and Calgary.
25. Banff National Park is one of the most popular parks in Canada.
26. Many towns in the United States are built around squares.

Simple Subjects and Predicates

> ■ The **simple subject** of a sentence is the main word in the complete subject. The simple subject is a noun or a pronoun. Sometimes the simple subject is also the complete subject.   EXAMPLES: The southern **section** of our state/has many forests. **Forests**/are beautiful.
>
> ■ The **simple predicate** of a sentence is a verb within the complete predicate. The verb may be made up of one word or more than one word.   EXAMPLES: Dogs/**have** good hearing. Maria/**is going.**

■ **Draw a line between the complete subject and the complete predicate in each sentence below. Then underline the simple subject once and the simple predicate twice.**

1. The different meanings for that word/cover half of a dictionary page.

2. A valuable oil is made from peanuts.

3. A beautiful highway winds through the Catskill Mountains.

4. The woman in the black dress studied the painting for over an hour.

5. The meadowlark builds its nest on the ground.

6. The making of ice cream can be much fun.

7. Many stories have been written about the old Spanish Main, the northern coast of South America.

8. His answer to the question was incorrect.

9. Every sentence should begin with a capital letter.

10. The rotation of the earth on its axis causes day and night.

11. In Norway, a narrow inlet of the sea between cliffs is called a fjord.

12. The Dutch cultivated large fields of tulips and hyacinths.

13. The two treasury mints in the United States are located in Philadelphia and Denver.

14. Benjamin Franklin's *Poor Richard's Almanac* is filled with wise sayings.

15. The warm climate of Jamaica attracts many winter tourists.

16. That movie has been shown on television many times.

17. Acres of wheat rippled in the breeze.

18. That mechanic completed the job in record time.

19. The people in that picture were boarding a plane for London.

20. One can find rocks of fantastic shapes in the Garden of the Gods, near Colorado Springs, Colorado.

21. The city of Albuquerque is five thousand feet above sea level.

22. The apple trees have fragrant blossoms.

23. Sequoias, the world's tallest trees, are found in California.

24. John Banister was an early botanist.

25. The tall pine trees hide our tiny cabin.

26. The woman filled the vase with colorful flowers.

Position of Subjects

- When the subject of a sentence comes before the verb, the sentence is in **natural order.**   EXAMPLE: Henry went to the park.
- When the verb or part of the verb comes before the subject, the sentence is in **inverted order.**   EXAMPLES: Here are the calculators. Down came the rain.
- Many questions are in inverted order.   EXAMPLE: Where is the restaurant?
- Sometimes the subject of a sentence is not expressed, as in a command or request. The understood subject is you.   EXAMPLES: Call about the job now. (You) call about the job now.

■ **Rewrite each inverted sentence in natural order. Underline the simple subject once and the simple predicate twice. Add you as the subject to commands or requests.**

1. When is the movie playing?

   _____

2. Never will I forget my first train trip.

   _____

3. Here is the picture I want to buy.

   _____

4. Seldom has he been ill.

   _____

5. Out went the lights.

   _____

6. There were bookcases on all sides of the room.

   _____

7. Take the roast from the oven.

   _____

8. Around the sharp curve swerved the speeding car.

   _____

9. Get out of the swimming pool.

   _____

10. Study for the spelling test.

    _____

11. There are two children in the pool.

    _____

Compound Subjects and Predicates

> ■ A **compound subject** is made up of two or more simple subjects.
>   EXAMPLE: **Matt** and **Jan**/are great swimmers.
> ■ A **compound predicate** is made up of two or more simple predicates.
>   EXAMPLE: The dog/**ran** and **barked** with joy.

A. Draw a line between the complete subject and the complete predicate in each sentence. Underline the compound subject once or the compound predicate twice in each sentence.

1. Lewis and Clark blazed a trail across the North American continent.

2. The rose and the jasmine are important flowers for perfume manufacturing.

3. Kelly and Amy went with us.

4. Chris swept the floor, dusted the furniture, and washed the windows.

5. Empires flourish and decay.

6. The level of the lake rises and falls several times each year.

7. Juanita and her brother are excellent skaters.

8. Dwight D. Eisenhower and Douglas MacArthur were famous American generals.

9. He turned slowly and then answered my question.

10. Museums, libraries, and art galleries are found in many cities.

11. The typewriters, the desks, and the chairs are all new.

12. The plants grew tall and flowered.

13. Stephanie and Teresa worked hard.

14. He ran and slid into third base.

15. The sales clerk added up the numbers and wrote down the total.

16. Reading and baking are her favorite pastimes.

17. Mary drank iced tea and ate a sandwich.

18. Cars and trucks sped past.

19. Red and blue are his favorite colors.

B. Write two sentences containing compound subjects.

1. _____

2. _____

C. Write two sentences containing compound predicates.

1. _____

2. _____

Combining Sentences

- Two sentences in which the subjects are different and the predicates are the same can be combined into one sentence. The two subjects are joined by <u>and</u>. EXAMPLE: **The sun** is part of our solar system. **The nine planets** are part of our solar system. **The sun and nine planets** are part of our solar system.
- Two sentences in which the subjects are the same and the predicates are different can be combined into one sentence. The two predicates may be joined by <u>or</u>, <u>and</u>, or <u>but</u>. EXAMPLE: The planets **are the largest bodies moving around the sun.** The planets **have a total of 34 moons.** The planets **are the largest bodies moving around the sun and have a total of 34 moons.**

■ **Combine each pair of sentences below. Underline the compound subject or the compound predicate in each sentence that you write.**

1. The nine planets in our solar system vary in size. The nine planets in our solar system are at different distances from the sun.

_____

_____

2. Mercury does not have any moons. Venus does not have any moons.

_____

3. Venus is similar in some ways to the earth. Venus is much hotter than the earth.

_____

4. Pluto is the farthest planet from the sun. Pluto takes 248 years to revolve around the sun.

_____

5. Planets revolve around the sun in regular paths. Planets also rotate and spin like tops.

_____

_____

6. Mercury revolves around the sun in less than a year. Venus revolves around the sun in less than a year.

_____

7. The solar system may have been formed in a collision between the sun and another star. The solar system may have come from a cloud of gas.

_____

_____

> - The **direct object** tells who or what receives the action of the verb. The direct object is a noun or pronoun that follows an action verb.
>
> EXAMPLE: Those countries export **coffee.**
>
> (with DO written above **coffee**)

- **Underline the verb in each sentence. Then write <u>DO</u> above each direct object.**

1. Juanita's good driving prevented an accident.

2. Every person should have an appreciation of music.

3. Gene, pass the potatoes, please.

4. Do not waste your time on this project.

5. James, did you keep those coupons?

6. Geraldo collects foreign stamps.

7. Eli Whitney invented the cotton gin.

8. Answer my question.

9. We are picking trophies for our bowling league.

10. Who invented the steamboat?

11. I am reading Hemingway's *The Old Man and the Sea.*

12. The North Star guides sailors.

13. The Phoenicians gave the alphabet to civilization.

14. Every person should study world history.

15. Who made this cake?

16. Can you find a direct object in this sentence?

17. Who wrote the story of Johnny Tremain?

18. We bought several curios for our friends.

19. Tamara read the minutes of our last club meeting.

20. Did you ever make a time budget of your own?

21. Mountains have often affected the history of a nation.

22. Emma and Joe baked a pie.

- The **indirect object** is the noun or pronoun that tells to whom or for whom an action is done. In order to have an indirect object, a sentence must have a direct object.
- The indirect object is usually placed between the action verb and the direct object.
  EXAMPLE: Who gave **me** this **box** of grapefruit?

- **Underline the verb in each sentence. Then write DO above the direct object and IO above the indirect object.**

1. The pitcher threw David a fast ball.

2. We gave the usher our tickets.

3. The doctor handed Chris the prescription.

4. Mr. Lewis sold us a set of encyclopedias.

5. Have you written Andrea the time of our arrival?

6. The supervisor paid the employee a high salary.

7. Experience should teach us wisdom.

8. Who sent Amy that long letter?

9. Maria, show us that magic trick.

10. I gave the cashier the money for our tickets.

11. Many years ago, a clever writer gave us the story of Robinson Crusoe.

12. A guide always shows visitors the interesting things in this museum.

13. Working crossword puzzles gives many people hours of enjoyment.

14. Carlos, give the group a lecture on saving money.

15. The study of space travel has brought us many new inventions.

16. Dale, please take Sandra these books.

17. Mrs. Yonge gave Joanne several plants.

18. Please give me a drink of water.

19. Who gave the United States flag the name of Old Glory?

20. Will you give me those instructions again?

Independent and Subordinate Clauses

■ A **clause** is a group of words that contains a subject and a predicate. There are two kinds of clauses: **independent clauses** and **subordinate clauses.**

■ An **independent clause** can stand alone as a sentence because it expresses a complete thought.
  EXAMPLE: **He recovered the watch** that he had lost.

A. Underline the independent clause in each sentence below.

1. We arrived late because we couldn't find the theater.

2. The play started before we found our seats.

3. We got one of the special programs that were being sold.

4. When the play was over, the audience applauded.

5. After we saw the show, we went for a walk.

6. Although the night was cool, the walk was enjoyable.

7. While we were walking, I noticed the moon.

8. Since it was a full moon, it was shining brightly.

9. We walked along the lake until it became very late.

10. By the time I got home, it was almost midnight.

■ A **subordinate clause** has a subject and predicate but cannot stand alone as a sentence because it does not express a complete thought.

■ A subordinate clause must be combined with an independent clause to make a sentence.
  EXAMPLE: We started **when the sun rose.**

B. Underline the subordinate clause in each sentence below.

1. Japan is a country where some trains travel at very fast speeds.

2. The airplane that we saw can land in only a few airports in this country.

3. Henry Hudson discovered the river that bears his name.

4. When you respect others, you win respect for yourself.

5. Diego found the new job that was perfect for him.

6. Colleen is the one who was elected without a run-off.

7. The coin that I purchased is an old French crown.

8. When I awoke, it was broad daylight.

9. Those who would control others must first control themselves.

10. The camel is the only pack animal that can stand the test of the Sahara.

- An **adjective clause** is a subordinate clause that modifies a noun or a pronoun. It answers the adjective question <u>Which one?</u> or <u>What kind?</u> It usually modifies the word directly preceding it. Most adjective clauses begin with a **relative pronoun.** A relative pronoun relates an adjective clause to the noun or pronoun that the clause modifies. <u>Who</u>, <u>whom</u>, <u>whose</u>, <u>which</u>, and <u>that</u> are relative pronouns.
  EXAMPLE: Always do the work **that is assigned to you.**
                                      adjective clause
- An **adverb clause** is a subordinate clause that modifies a verb, an adjective, or another adverb. It answers the adverb question <u>How?</u> <u>Under what condition?</u> or <u>Why?</u> Words that introduce adverb clauses are called **subordinating conjunctions.** The many subordinating conjunctions include such words as <u>when</u>, <u>after</u>, <u>before</u>, <u>since</u>, <u>although</u>, and <u>because</u>.
  EXAMPLE: We left **when the storm clouds gathered.**
                              adverb clause

A. Underline the subordinate clause. Then write <u>adjective</u> or <u>adverb</u> on the line.

_____ 1. John Paul Jones was a hero whose bravery won many victories.

_____ 2. The person who reads the most books will get a prize.

_____ 3. He overslept because he hadn't set the alarm.

_____ 4. Give a rousing cheer when our team comes off the field.

_____ 5. The parrot repeats many things that he hears.

_____ 6. The picnic that we planned was canceled.

B. Add a subordinate clause beginning with the word in parentheses to each independent clause below.

1. The package was gone   (when) _____

_____

2. A depot is a place   (where) _____

_____

3. Brad and I cannot go now   (because) _____

_____

4. Tell me the name of the person   (who) _____

_____

Compound and Complex Sentences

- A **compound sentence** consists of two or more independent clauses. Each independent clause in a compound sentence can stand alone as a separate sentence. The independent clauses are usually joined by <u>and</u>, <u>but</u>, <u>so</u>, <u>or</u>, for, or <u>yet</u> and a comma.

    EXAMPLE: I like to dance, but Jim likes to sing.

- Sometimes a **semicolon (;)** is used to join the independent clauses in a compound sentence.

    EXAMPLE: I like to dance; Jim likes to sing.

- A **complex sentence** consists of one independent clause and one or more subordinate clauses.

    EXAMPLE: **When the fire alarm went off,** everyone left the building.
    subordinate clause

A. Write CP before each compound sentence. Write CX before each complex sentence.

_____ 1. Our team didn't always win, but we always tried to be good sports.

_____ 2. You may stay, but I am going home.

_____ 3. The rangers who serve in Yellowstone Park know every inch of the ground.

_____ 4. That statement may be correct, but it isn't very polite.

_____ 5. We will meet whenever we can.

_____ 6. The pass was thrown perfectly, but Carlos was too well guarded to catch it.

_____ 7. The toga was worn by ancient Roman youths when they reached the age of twelve.

_____ 8. That song, which is often heard on the radio, was written years ago.

_____ 9. They cannot come for dinner, but they will be here later.

_____ 10. My brother likes dogs, but I prefer cats.

_____ 11. The engine is the heart of the submarine, and the periscope is the eye.

_____ 12. I will call you when it arrives.

_____ 13. Those people who camped here were messy.

_____ 14. Edison was only thirty years old when he invented the talking machine.

_____ 15. She crept silently, for she was afraid.

_____ 16. Move the table, but be careful with it.

_____ 17. Bolivia is the only South American country that does not have a port.

_____ 18. How many stars were in the flag that Key saw "by the dawn's early light"?

_____ 19. The octopus gets its name from two Greek words that mean <u>eight</u> and <u>feet</u>.

_____ 20. You may place the order, but we cannot guarantee shipment.

_____ 21. After the sun set, we built a campfire.

_____ 22. We made hamburgers for dinner, and then we toasted marshmallows.

_____ 23. Some people sang songs; others played games.

_____ 24. When it started to rain, everyone took shelter in their tents.

B. Put brackets [ ] around the independent clauses in each compound sentence below. Then underline the simple subject once and the simple predicate twice in each clause.

1. [The <u>streets</u> <u>are</u> filled with cars], but [the <u>sidewalks</u> <u>are</u> empty].

2. Those apples are too sour to eat, but those pears are perfect.

3. She studies hard, but she saves some time to enjoy herself.

4. They lost track of time, so they were late.

5. Eric had not studied, so he failed the test.

6. Yesterday it rained all day, but today the sun is shining.

7. I set the alarm to get up early, but I couldn't get up.

8. They may sing and dance until dawn, but they will be exhausted.

9. My friend moved to Texas, and I will miss her.

10. They arrived at the theater early, but there was still a long line.

11. Lisa took her dog to the veterinarian, but his office was closed.

12. The black cat leaped, but fortunately it didn't catch the bird.

13. I found a baseball in the bushes, and I gave it to my brother.

14. We loaded the cart with groceries, and we went to the checkout.

15. The stadium was showered with lights, but the stands were empty.

16. The small child whimpered, and her mother hugged her.

17. The dark clouds rolled in, and then it began to rain.

C. In each complex sentence below, underline the subordinate clause.

1. The hummingbird is the only bird that can fly backward.

2. The cat that is sitting in the window is mine.

3. The car that is parked outside is new.

4. Jack, who is a football star, is class president.

5. Bonnie, who is an artist, is also studying computer science.

6. John likes food that is cooked in the microwave.

7. The composer who wrote the music comes from Germany.

8. We missed seeing him because we were late.

9. When Jake arrives, we will tell him what happened.

10. She walked slowly because she had hurt her leg.

11. When she walked to the podium, everyone applauded.

12. If animals could talk, they might have a lot to tell.

13. Many roads that were built in our city are no longer traveled.

14. My address book, which is bright red, is gone.

15. Ann, who is from Georgia, just started working here today.

16. The crowd cheered when the player came to bat.

17. When he hit the ball, everyone cheered.

Lesson 22

Correcting Run-on Sentences

- Two or more independent clauses that are run together without the correct punctuation are called a **run-on sentence.**
    - EXAMPLE: Your brain is an amazing organ you could not read without it.
- One way to correct a run-on sentence is to separate it into two sentences.
    - EXAMPLE: Your brain is an amazing organ. You could not read without it.
- Another way to correct a run-on sentence is to make it into a compound sentence.
    - EXAMPLE: Your brain is an amazing organ, and you could not read without it.
- Another way to correct a run-on sentence is to use a semicolon.
    - EXAMPLE: Your brain is an amazing organ; you could not read without it.

- **Correct each run-on sentence below by writing it as two sentences or as a compound sentence.**

1. The brain is surrounded by three membranes the skull encloses the brain and these three membranes.

   _____

   _____

2. The brain reaches its full size by the time a person is twenty at that time, it weighs about three pounds.

   _____

   _____

3. The brain helps a person see, hear, touch, smell, and taste it also makes it possible for one to remember and forget, talk and write, and feel emotions.

   _____

   _____

4. The brain has three main parts these parts are the cerebrum, the cerebellum, and the brain stem.

   _____

   _____

5. A computer is like a human brain however, computers cannot perform all of the functions of a human brain.

   _____

   _____

   _____

Lesson 23

Expanding Sentences

- Sentences can be **expanded** by adding details to make them clearer and more interesting. EXAMPLE: The dog ran. The **big black** dog ran **barking into the street.**
- Details added to sentences may answer these questions: When? Where? How? How often? To what degree? What kind? Which? How many?

A. Expand each sentence below by adding details to answer the questions shown in parentheses. Write the expanded sentence on the line.

1. The crew was ready for liftoff.   (Which? When?)

_____

2. The shuttle was launched.   (What kind? Where?)

_____

3. The engines roared.   (How many? To what degree?)

_____

4. The spacecraft shot up.   (How? Where?)

_____

5. The astronauts studied the control panels.   (How many? Where?)

_____

B. Decide how each of the following sentences can be expanded. Write your expanded sentence on the line.

1. The singer ran onto the stage.

_____

2. The fans leaped up and cheered.

_____

3. She began to sing.

_____

4. She strummed the guitar.

_____

5. The loudspeakers blared.

_____

6. The fans began dancing.

_____

A. Label each sentence as follows: Write **D** for declarative, **IN** for interrogative, **IM** for imperative, or **E** for exclamatory. Punctuate each sentence correctly.

_____ 1. Is that the book I wanted____

_____ 2. Please, give it to me____

_____ 3. I read this book____

_____ 4. That's a fantastic book ____

_____ 5. Who is your favorite author____

_____ 6. John, put those books in the box____

_____ 7. We'll sell them at the garage sale____

_____ 8. Most people would enjoy them____

_____ 9. I know I did ____

_____ 10. Will we make enough money ____

B. Underline the words in each sentence that are identified in parentheses.

1. (complete subject)   The leaves on the trees in the park turned orange and yellow.

2. (simple subject)   The tourists came to see the changing colors.

3. (direct object)   The children gathered the leaves.

4. (complete predicate)   Some artists painted the colorful scene.

5. (simple predicate)   Camera buffs snapped photographs.

6. (compound predicate)   Dogs jumped and rolled in the piles of crackling leaves.

7. (compound subject)   Adults and children were delighted by the scene.

8. (indirect object)   A toddler handed his mother a bright orange leaf.

9. (direct object)   She happily took the leaf.

10. (indirect object)   Then she gave him a hug.

C. Draw a line between the complete subject and the complete predicate in each sentence. Underline the simple subject once and the simple predicate twice.

1. The crowd of protesting citizens marched down the street.

2. Kara felt the first drops of rain on her face.

3. Under the fence crawled the frightened coyote.

4. All the patrol cars are parked near the police station.

D. Combine each pair of sentences below. Underline the compound subject or the compound predicate in each sentence that you write.

1. The leaves of some trees turn bright colors in the autumn. Some leaves fall off in the autumn.

_____

2. Linda refuses to watch violent movies. Judy refuses to watch violent movies.

_____

3. Tom washed his car. Tom waxed his car.

_____

4. James and Kathryn ride to work together. Kathryn and Kamal ride to work together.

_____

E. Underline the independent clause in each sentence below.

1. After the first act ended, we left the theater.

2. Pat used her computer for the design that won the contest.

3. By the way they were talking, we knew they weren't going.

4. Canada and the United States share a long border that runs east and west.

F. Underline the subordinate clause in each sentence below.

1. I was at the station when the train arrived.

2. The letter that she found had been mailed two years earlier.

3. After he lit the charcoal, he put on the steaks.

4. The heel broke off her shoe while she was walking.

G. Underline the subordinate clause in each sentence. Then identify the clause by writing adjective or adverb on the line.

_____ 1. The person who writes the funniest limerick will appear on television.

_____ 2. She burned the cookies because she wasn't paying attention.

_____ 3. Stand up when the judge enters the courtroom.

_____ 4. He remembered the dress that she wore to the dance.

H. Write CP after each compound sentence and CX after each complex sentence.

1. The bicycle that I wanted is displayed in the window. _____

2. I am going to save my money, and then I'll buy it. _____

3. My boss, who is a generous man, said he would let me work more often. _____

4. I will work more hours whenever I can. _____

5. I want the one that is a slick, silver mountain bike. _____

I. Correct the run-on sentences below.

1. Janet brought the DVD to my house I popped it into the DVD player.

_____

2. Teresa went to the party she took salad and it was good.

_____

3. What was in the salad it contained fresh fruits and walnuts.

_____

4. She gave me the recipe I can copy it for you.

_____

A. Read the sentences in the box. Then answer the questions below.

> **A.** We just rented and moved into an apartment next to the firehouse.
> **B.** The clanging bells and whining sirens go off day and night.
> **C.** The continuous noise is incredible!
> **D.** Shut all the windows.
> **E.** Did you give the landlord the check yet?

1. _____ Which sentence has a compound subject?

2. _____ Which sentence has a compound predicate?

3. _____ Which sentences have direct objects?

4. _____ Which sentence has an indirect object?

5. _____ Which sentence is interrogative?

6. _____ Which sentences are declarative?

7. _____ Which sentence is exclamatory?

8. _____ Which sentence is imperative?

9. What is the complete subject of C? _____

10. What is the simple subject of C? _____

11. What is the complete predicate of B? _____

12. What is the simple predicate of B? _____

B. Underline the independent clause, and circle the subordinate clause in each sentence below.

1. We planned this trip a month ago, after the holidays were over.

2. After we planned the trip, we posted a sign-up sheet.

3. Here is the sign-up sheet that was hanging in the club room.

4. Everyone who is in the ski club plans to take the trip.

5. When everyone packs carefully, the ski gear fits on the bus.

6. When the bus arrives, we will hand out the tickets.

C. Combine each pair of sentences below to form a compound sentence.

1. It is sunny out today. It's still too cold to go to the beach.

_____

2. Maria can't go with us today. She can come tomorrow.

_____

3. Carol said she would meet us. I'll tell her we aren't going.

_____

4. We could go to see that adventure movie. We could go see the new exhibit.

_____

D. Rewrite each inverted sentence below in natural order.

1. Reported on a television bulletin was the news of the storm.

_____

2. Into the hangar taxied the small airplane.

_____

3. Down the ramp came the tired passengers.

_____

E. Create complex sentences by adding a subordinate clause or an independent clause to each group of words.

1. She looked sad _____

2. When she thought about what she said _____

3. This was the time _____

4. After she wrote her apology _____

5. When she wrote it _____

6. Before we left the house _____

F. Rewrite the paragraph below, correcting the run-on sentences.

      In space medicine research, new types of miniature equipment for checking how the body functions have been developed on the spacecraft, astronauts' breathing rates, heartbeats, and blood pressure are taken with miniature devices no larger than a pill. These devices detect the information and transmit it to scientists back on Earth they allow the scientists to monitor astronauts' body responses from a long distance and over long periods of time.

_____

_____

_____

_____

_____

G. Read the two sentences below. Then expand each sentence by adding details to make the sentence clearer and more interesting.

1. The acrobats climbed the ladder.

_____

2. They began their act.

_____

Common and Proper Nouns

> - There are two main classes of nouns: **common** and **proper nouns.**
> - A **common noun** names any one of a class of objects.
>   EXAMPLES: woman, city, tree
> - A **proper noun** names a particular person, place, or thing. It begins with
>   a capital letter.
>   EXAMPLES: Ms. Patel, Chicago, Empire State Building

A. Underline each noun. Then write C or P above it to show whether it is a common or proper noun.

      P   C

1. <u>Maria</u> is my <u>sister</u>.

2. Honolulu is the chief city and capital of Hawaii.

3. Rainbow Natural Bridge is hidden away in the wild mountainous part of southern Utah.

4. The Declaration of Independence is often called the birth certificate of the United States.

5. Abraham Lincoln, Edgar Allan Poe, and Frederic Chopin were born in the same year.

B. Write a proper noun suggested by each common noun.

1. country _____

2. book _____

3. governor _____

4. state _____

5. athlete _____

6. school _____

7. actor _____

8. day _____

9. car _____

10. lake _____

11. singer _____

12. holiday _____

13. newspaper _____

14. river _____

C. Write a sentence using each proper noun and the common noun for its class.

1. Mexico   <u>Mexico</u> is another <u>country</u> in North America.

2. December _____

3. Alaska _____

4. Thanksgiving Day _____

5. Abraham Lincoln _____

6. Tuesday _____

Concrete, Abstract, and Collective Nouns

■ A **concrete noun** names things you can see and touch.
   EXAMPLES: apple, dog, fork, book, computer
■ An **abstract noun** names an idea, quality, action, or feeling.
   EXAMPLES: bravery, wickedness, goodness
■ A **collective noun** names a group of persons or things.
   EXAMPLES: crowd, congress, public, United States

■ **Classify each common noun as concrete, collective, or abstract.**

1. humor _____

2. kindness _____

3. army _____

4. danger _____

5. committee _____

6. towel _____

7. jury _____

8. audience _____

9. bird _____

10. orchestra _____

11. fear _____

12. family _____

13. happiness _____

14. truck _____

15. audience _____

16. honesty _____

17. bracelet _____

18. society _____

19. album _____

20. courage _____

21. faculty _____

22. club _____

23. photograph _____

24. poverty _____

25. class _____

26. swarm _____

27. table _____

28. goodness _____

29. flock _____

30. radio _____

31. mob _____

32. patience _____

33. herd _____

34. banana _____

35. staff _____

36. mercy _____

37. calculator _____

38. coyote _____

39. generosity _____

40. scissors _____

41. sorrow _____

42. independence _____

Singular and Plural Nouns

■ The following chart shows how to change **singular nouns** into **plural nouns**.

Noun	Plural Form	Examples
Most nouns	Add -s	ship, ships nose, noses
Nouns ending in a consonant and -y	Change the -y to -i, and add -es	sky, skies navy, navies
Nouns ending in -o	Add -s or -es	hero, heroes piano, pianos
Most nouns ending in -f or -fe	Change the -f or -fe to -ves	half, halves
Most nouns ending in -ch, -sh, -s, or -x	Add -es	bench, benches bush, bushes tax, taxes
Many two-word or three-word compound nouns	Add -s to the principle word	son-in-law, sons-in-law
Nouns with the same form in the singular and plural	No change	sheep
Nouns with no singular form	No change	scissors
Nouns with irregular plurals	Change the entire word	foot, feet child, children
Figures, symbols, signs, letters, and words considered as words	Add an apostrophe and -s	m, m's 5, 5's and, and's

A. Write the plural for each singular noun.

1. county _____

2. pony _____

3. tomato _____

4. banjo _____

5. match _____

6. window _____

7. century _____

8. trench _____

9. bookcase _____

10. video _____

11. radio _____

12. farm _____

13. fly _____

14. hero _____

15. dress _____

16. boot _____

17. desk _____

18. daisy _____

B. Write the singular form of each word below.

1. mouthfuls _____

2. proofs _____

3. 6's _____

4. calves _____

5. knives _____

6. Joneses _____

7. children _____

8. geese _____

9. wolves _____

10. roofs _____

11. gentlemen _____

12. editors-in-chief _____

13. +'s _____

14. cupfuls _____

15. trout _____

16. mice _____

C. Fill each blank with the plural form of the word in parentheses. You may use a dictionary to check spellings.

1. (box) Please store these _____ in the garage.

2. (city) Can you name the four largest _____ in your state?

3. (deer) The photographers brought back photos of three _____.

4. (flash) The vivid _____ of lightning frightened everyone.

5. (coach) That football team employs five _____.

6. (church) Our small town has several beautiful _____.

7. (potato) Hot _____ were used as hand warmers in colonial days.

8. (e) How many _____ are in the word <u>Tennessee</u>?

9. (O'Keefe) The _____ are having a recital tonight.

10. (fish) Where did you catch those _____?

11. (scarf) Dale gave me three _____.

12. (n) Cynthia, don't make your _____ look like <u>u</u>'s.

13. (radio) Kirk listens to two _____ so he can hear all the news.

14. (ox) The _____ wore a yoke around their necks.

15. (pilot) Those _____ flew four round trips a day.

16. (90) The teacher gave three _____ on the math test.

17. (woman) A dozen _____ attended the conference.

18. (i) Be sure to always dot your _____.

> - A **possessive noun** shows possession of the noun that follows.
>   EXAMPLES: Gerry's football, Donna's gloves
> - Form the possessive of most singular nouns by adding an apostrophe
>   (') and -s.
>   EXAMPLES: José's pillow, Sandy's eyes
> - Form the possessive of most plural nouns ending in -s by adding only
>   an apostrophe.
>   EXAMPLES: birds' nest, lions' den
> - Form the possessive of plural nouns that do not end in -s by adding
>   apostrophe and -s.
>   EXAMPLES: men's wear

- **Underline the possessive nouns in each sentence.**

1. Steve's glasses are on my desk.

2. Mary is wearing her mother's gold bracelet.

3. My friends' club will meet at our house Monday night.

4. The woman's first statement caused us to change our minds.

5. We have formed a collector's club.

6. Rosa's brother found the child's lost puppy.

7. The Warrens' store was damaged by the recent storm.

8. What are the vice-president's duties?

9. When does the new mayor's term of office begin?

10. Lee, Tony's notebook is on your desk.

11. We went to the women's department.

12. The family's income was reduced.

13. Our day's work is done.

14. The lifeguards' heroism was rewarded.

15. Our team's defeat did not discourage us.

16. Has Joanna opened a children's store?

17. Juan's cooking is improving.

18. We borrowed Jim's hammer.

19. May I see Calvin's picture?

20. I'll meet you at the Lees'.

21. Lucy visited Mark's college.

22. Frank's telephone call was about Jean's accident.

23. Mr. Clark stood at his neighbors' gate.

24. Is that the Masons' parking place?

25. The United States' flag has stars and stripes.

- An **appositive** is a noun or pronoun that identifies or explains the noun or pronoun it follows.
  EXAMPLE: My German friend, **Ulrike**, is coming to visit me next month.
- An **appositive phrase** consists of an appositive and its modifiers.
  EXAMPLE: Peter's school, **the junior high,** is sponsoring a dance.
- Use commas to set off an appositive or an appositive phrase that is not essential to the meaning of the sentence.
  EXAMPLE: Rico's nephew, **a twelve-year-old,** delivers newspapers.
- Do not use commas if the appositive is essential to the meaning of the sentence.
  EXAMPLE: The artist **Picasso** is my favorite.

- **Underline each appositive word or phrase, and circle the noun it identifies.**

1. (Jan Matzeliger), the inventor of the first shoemaking machine, was born in South America.

2. Niagara Falls, the waterfalls in New York, is not the tallest in the country.

3. Harvard, the oldest university in the United States, is in Massachusetts.

4. My brother Jim lives in Connecticut.

5. Diane Feinstein, a mayor of San Francisco, was San Francisco's first woman mayor.

6. The Sears Tower, one of the tallest buildings in the world, is in Chicago.

7. Scott's cousin Liz sells antique cars.

8. Leontyne Price, the opera singer, was born in Mississippi.

9. The Pilgrim's ship the *Mayflower* had a stormy voyage.

10. Tom's dog Jasmine likes to swim.

11. Dr. Miller, our family physician, is attending a convention with her husband.

12. The swimmer Mark Spitz won seven gold medals in one Olympics.

13. Fort Worth, a city in Texas, is almost midway between the Atlantic and the Pacific.

14. Aunt Lee, my father's sister, is coming to visit.

15. Mr. Diddon, coach of the hockey team, has never had a losing season.

16. Monticello, Jefferson's home, is an example of colonial architecture.

17. The inventor Thomas Edison is responsible for many electrical breakthroughs.

18. Athens, the leading city of ancient Greece, was a center of culture.

19. The Aztec king Montezuma was captured by Cortez.

20. The boll weevil, a small beetle, causes great damage to cotton.

21. The Hoover Dam, a dam in the Colorado River, took five years to build.

22. Antares, a star many times larger than the sun, is the red star in Scorpio.

23. The composer Mozart lived a short but productive life.

24. That is a copperhead, one of the four poisonous snakes found in the United States.

25. Mt. McKinley, a rugged mountain, is the tallest mountain in North America.

- A **verb** is a word that expresses action, being, or state of being.
  EXAMPLES: Leo **traveled** to Europe. Maura **is** an accountant.
- A verb has four principal parts: **present, present participle, past,** and **past participle.**
- For regular verbs, form the present participle by adding -ing to the present. Use a form of the helping verb be with the present participle.
- Form the past and past participle by adding -ed to the present. Use a form of the helping verb have with the past participle.
  EXAMPLES:

Present	Present Participle	Past	Past Participle
listen	(is) listening	listened	(have, had, has) listened
help	(is) helping	helped	(have, had, has) helped
change	(is) changing	changed	(have, had, has) changed

- Irregular verbs form their past and past participle in other ways. A dictionary shows the principal parts of these verbs.

- **Write the present participle, past, and past participle for each verb.**

PRESENT	PRESENT PARTICIPLE	PAST	PAST PARTICIPLE
1. scatter	(is) scattering	scattered	(have, had, has) scattered
2. express			
3. paint			
4. call			
5. cook			
6. observe			
7. look			
8. walk			
9. ramble			
10. shout			
11. notice			
12. order			
13. gaze			
14. borrow			
15. start			
16. work			

Verb Phrases

> ■ A **verb phrase** consists of a main verb and one or more **helping verbs.**
> A helping verb is also called an **auxiliary verb.** In a verb phrase, the
> helping verb or verbs precede the main verb.
> EXAMPLE: Liz **has been** reading a mystery.
> ■ The helping verbs are
>> am, are, is, was, were, be, being, been
>> has, have, had
>> do, does, did
>> can, could, must, may, might
>> shall, should, will, would

A. Underline each verb or verb phrase, and circle each helping verb in the sentences below.

1. Most people have heard the story of Jonathan Chapman.

2. He was born in 1775 and has become an American legend.

3. You may have heard of him as the barefooted, lovable Johnny Appleseed.

4. As Jonathan Chapman, he had grown up in the woods near Boston, Massachusetts.

5. He had learned about fruit trees in the orchards near his family's farm.

6. He was always interested in the stories he had heard about the Great West.

7. As a young man, he had declared, "I will go west to Pennsylvania and plant my own orchard."

8. Jonathan had done just that, but in a few years, the wilderness had moved farther west.

9. "What should I do now?" Jonathan asked himself.

10. "I will plant other apple orchards!" was his answer.

11. Jonathan could not remain content.

12. Soon he was traveling with the other settlers as the frontier pushed farther and farther west.

13. People called him Johnny Appleseed, that odd man who did not have a home.

14. He would sleep out in the open with his beloved trees.

B. Use each verb phrase in a sentence.

1. should learn _____

2. will occur _____

3. may find _____

4. have tried _____

5. can make _____

6. will go _____

- The **tense** of a verb tells the time of the action or being. There are six main tenses: **present, past, future, present perfect, past perfect,** and **future prefect.**
- Present tense tells about what is happening now.
  EXAMPLES: Emily **sings.** The kittens **are playing.**
- Past tense tells about something that happened in the past.
  EXAMPLES: Emily **sang** in the play. The kittens **were playing** on the porch.
- Future tense tells about something that will happen in the future.
  EXAMPLES: Emily **will sing** in the play. The kittens **will play** on the porch.
- Present perfect tense tells about something that occurred at an indefinite time in the past.
  EXAMPLE: Emily **has sung** the song.
  It is also used to tell about something that began in the past and continues in the present.
  EXAMPLE: The kittens **have been playing** on the porch.
- Past perfect tense tells about something completed at some past time before something else.
  EXAMPLES: Emily **had sung** before you arrived. The kittens **had been playing** on the porch until Tom came home.
- Future perfect tense tells about something that will be completed before some definite future time.
  EXAMPLES: Emily **will have finished** singing by eight o'clock.

- Underline each verb or verb phrase. Write <u>present</u>, <u>past</u>, <u>future</u>, <u>present perfect</u>, <u>past perfect</u>, or <u>future perfect</u>.

1. I <u>brought</u> these vegetables. _____past_____

2. Yes, I know her. _____

3. They will close the office tomorrow. _____

4. The work will continue for several days. _____

5. His friend has donated the painting to the museum. _____

6. Alex had told us many stories about his travels. _____

7. Jesse Owens was a famous track star. _____

8. She sings well. _____

9. Mark will have paid for the meal. _____

10. I will have been in St. Louis for a week. _____

11. The neighborhood children had been playing baseball. _____

12. I have anchored the boat. _____

A. Write the principal parts of each verb. You may use a dictionary.

PRESENT	PRESENT PARTICIPLE	PAST	PAST PARTICIPLE
1. do	is doing	did	has done
2. come			
3. eat			
4. go			
5. see			
6. take			

B. Fill in the blank with the correct form of the verb in parentheses.

1. (see) I had never _____ the waterfall before.

2. (see) Have you ever _____ a helicopter?

3. (take) Laura is _____ the hammer with her.

4. (see) We have just _____ a passenger train going over the bridge.

5. (eat) Haven't you _____ your lunch?

6. (go) You should have _____ with us, Jerry.

7. (go) Jaime is _____ to a committee meeting.

8. (eat) Have you ever _____ a spiced olive?

9. (go) Julian has _____ to play a video game.

10. (take) Carey is _____ the photograph now.

11. (do) Who _____ the landscaping around this building?

12. (do) We have _____ a great deal of outside reading on the topic for discussion.

13. (take) Aren't we _____ the wrong road?

14. (come) People have _____ from every state to see the Carlsbad Caverns.

15. (eat) We had _____ different foods in different areas of the country.

16. (see) Thomas, you should have _____ the last game.

17. (come) Most of our people _____ this way on the way to the park.

18. (do) Matt _____ his best to beat his own record in the broad jump.

C. Write the principal parts of each verb. You may use a dictionary.

PRESENT	PRESENT PARTICIPLE	PAST	PAST PARTICIPLE
1. begin	_____	_____	_____
2. drink	_____	_____	_____
3. drive	_____	_____	_____
4. give	_____	_____	_____
5. run	_____	_____	_____

D. Fill in the blank with the correct form of the verb in parentheses.

1. (give)   My friend _____ this poem to me.

2. (run)   The excited children _____ down the street.

3. (begin)   Work on the new building had _____ this week.

4. (begin)   I _____ this project yesterday.

5. (drink)   Haven't you _____ some of this delicious fruit juice?

6. (drive)   Steven, have you ever _____ a car?

7. (give)   Gwendolyn Brooks has _____ us many interesting poems.

8. (begin)   The supervisor of the crew is _____ to explain the work orders.

9. (run)   Rachel, have you _____ into Aunt Sarah?

10. (run)   The girl _____ to meet her parents.

11. (begin)   That problem _____ last year.

12. (give)   James has _____ me a painting for my living room.

13. (begin)   Look, it is _____ to rain.

14. (run)   They _____ hard to get out of the rain.

15. (give)   Mrs. Williams has _____ me a job in her store.

16. (give)   Donald, who _____ you this watch?

17. (begin)   We haven't _____ eating all the bananas.

18. (drink)   Have you _____ from this cup?

19. (begin)   We _____ raking the leaves this morning.

20. (run)   Michelle is _____ in the 2-mile race.

E. Write the principal parts of each verb. You may use a dictionary.

PRESENT	PRESENT PARTICIPLE	PAST	PAST PARTICIPLE
1. grow	_____	_____	_____
2. know	_____	_____	_____
3. ring	_____	_____	_____
4. sing	_____	_____	_____
5. speak	_____	_____	_____

F. Fill in the blank with the correct form of the verb in parentheses.

1. (sing)   Have you ever _____ a solo?

2. (grow)   In several minutes, my eyes _____ accustomed to the dark.

3. (know)   Bob _____ the answer.

4. (grow)   It has _____ very cold during the last hour.

5. (sing)   Ricardo is _____ although his throat is sore.

6. (ring)   Why hasn't the bell _____?

7. (grow)   Lettuce had first _____ in China.

8. (speak)   Cynthia _____ to Jonathan yesterday.

9. (ring)   The carrier _____ the doorbell.

10. (speak)   Has Rafael _____ to you about his promotion?

11. (speak)   A police officer is _____ to a group of concerned citizens.

12. (sing)   Natalie and her sister _____ on a local TV program last week.

13. (know)   We have _____ the members of that family a long time.

14. (ring)   The mission bells _____ each morning last week.

15. (throw)   Have you _____ away this morning's paper?

16. (grow)   Charles, I believe you have _____ a prize-winning rose.

17. (know)   We have _____ Roberto's brother for three years.

18. (grow)   Because of the rains, the grass is _____ rapidly.

19. (ring)   We _____ the doorbell, but no one answered it.

20. (speak)   Joan has _____ of you quite often, Jeffrey.

G. Write the principal parts of each verb. You may use a dictionary.

PRESENT	PRESENT PARTICIPLE	PAST	PAST PARTICIPLE
1. blow	_____	_____	_____
2. break	_____	_____	_____
3. choose	_____	_____	_____
4. draw	_____	_____	_____
5. fly	_____	_____	_____

H. Fill in the blank with the correct form of the verb in parentheses.

1. (draw)   Kim has _____ many cartoons for the daily paper.

2. (blow)   The storm _____ tumbleweeds across the prairie.

3. (fly)   The tiny mockingbird is _____ from its nest.

4. (choose)   We _____ only willing persons for the committee.

5. (choose)   Our club has _____ a motto.

6. (blow)   Has the five o'clock whistle _____?

7. (break)   I accidentally _____ my sister's antique vase.

8. (break)   Her promise had not been _____.

9. (choose)   The coach is _____ the line-up for today's game.

10. (draw)   A famous artist _____ these sketches.

11. (break)   One of the windows in the house had _____ during the storm.

12. (break)   The handle of my hammer _____ while I was using it.

13. (choose)   Has anyone _____ the salad for lunch?

14. (break)   Suzanne _____ this chair yesterday.

15. (freeze)   Those pipes _____ last February.

16. (choose)   Do you think I have _____ wisely?

17. (break)   They _____ our winning streak last week.

18. (draw)   Have you _____ your map, Lee?

19. (break)   Who is _____ these windows?

20. (draw)   Their plans for the new house have been _____.

Unit 3, Grammar and Usage

I. Write the principal parts of each verb. You may use a dictionary.

PRESENT	PRESENT PARTICIPLE	PAST	PAST PARTICIPLE
1. become	_____	_____	_____
2. fall	_____	_____	_____
3. ride	_____	_____	_____
4. rise	_____	_____	_____
5. steal	_____	_____	_____
6. show	_____	_____	_____
7. sink	_____	_____	_____
8. swim	_____	_____	_____
9. tear	_____	_____	_____
10. wear	_____	_____	_____

J. Fill in the blank with the correct form of the verb in parentheses.

1. (ride) Have you ever _____ on a tractor?

2. (rise) The temperature has _____ ten degrees this afternoon.

3. (wear) We _____ our sweaters because the night air was very cool.

4. (steal) Look! Carolyn has _____ third base!

5. (ride) How far are we _____ today?

6. (swim) Jeanne is _____ around the pool.

7. (tear) The child _____ his jeans when he fell down.

8. (sink) When his boat _____, Crusoe was tossed about in the sea.

9. (steal) Our new car has been _____.

10. (ride) Have you ever _____ in an airplane?

11. (wear) This wire has almost been _____ in two.

12. (wear) I have _____ this coat for several winters.

13. (rise) The river recently _____ beyond the flood stage.

14. (rise) Diane has _____ from editor to president of the company.

15. (fall) All the pears have _____ from the tree.

Lesson 33

Mood

> - **Mood** is a form of the verb that shows the manner of doing or being. There are three types of moods: **indicative, subjunctive,** and **imperative.**
> - **Indicative mood** states a fact or asks a question.
>   EXAMPLES: Ben **came** Friday. How many **went** to the meeting?
> - **Subjunctive mood** can indicate a wish or a contrary-to-fact condition. Use <u>were</u> to express the subjunctive.
>   EXAMPLE: I would help you, if I **were** able. (I am not able.)
> - **Imperative mood** expresses a command or a request.
>   EXAMPLES: **Ask** no more questions. Let's **start** immediately.

- **Give the mood of each underlined word.**

1. <u>Come</u> here at once. _____

2. I <u>did</u> not <u>see</u> Carolyn. _____

3. If I <u>were</u> not so tired, I would go to a movie. _____

4. <u>Call</u> for him at once. _____

5. Where <u>has</u> Brittany <u>moved</u>? _____

6. Who <u>invented</u> the sewing machine? _____

7. Juanita <u>came</u> Saturday. _____

8. Paul wishes it <u>were</u> true. _____

9. <u>Come</u> here, Jennifer. _____

10. I wish it <u>were</u> summer. _____

11. <u>Be</u> home early. _____

12. <u>Ring</u> the bell immediately. _____

13. The members of the band <u>sold</u> birthday calendars. _____

14. If I <u>were</u> you, I'd stop that. _____

15. Zachary <u>likes</u> my new sweater. _____

16. My friends <u>painted</u> the entire house. _____

17. If this <u>were</u> a sunny day, I would go with you. _____

18. <u>Tell</u> us where you went. _____

19. He greeted me as though I <u>were</u> a stranger. _____

- There are two kinds of action verbs: **transitive** and **intransitive.**
- A transitive verb has a direct object.
  EXAMPLE: Columbus **discovered** America.
- An intransitive verb does not need an object to complete its meaning.
  Linking verbs are always intransitive.
  EXAMPLES: The wind **howled.** He **is** afraid.

A. Underline each verb, and classify it as transitive or intransitive.

1. We walked into the new school. _____intransitive_____

2. Ornithology is the study of birds. _____

3. Move those blocks now! _____

4. Everyone listened carefully. _____

5. The workers wore special uniforms. _____

6. We built a barbecue pit in our backyard. _____

7. What is the name of this picture? _____

8. He lives in Germany. _____

9. Who elected the principal of Stuart High? _____

10. Leroy paid the bill. _____

11. We send many good customers to them. _____

12. London is the capital city of Great Britain. _____

13. Frank drew many excellent cartoons. _____

14. We study hard for tests. _____

15. The frightened children cried loudly. _____

16. Lora made this poster. _____

17. Thousands of people ran in the race. _____

18. We learned three new songs. _____

19. The stray dogs barked. _____

20. Please bring me a book about famous Canadian scientists. _____

21. Joseph baked a lemon meringue pie. _____

B. Underline each verb or verb phrase, and classify it as transitive or intransitive.

1. The President of the United States signed the new law. _____

2. The workers repaired the telephone lines. _____

3. The factory shipped the shoes. _____

4. Wasteful cutting of timber may cause a shortage of lumber. _____

5. Wolf was Rip Van Winkle's sole friend. _____

6. The city of Mobile, Alabama, has a wonderful harbor. _____

7. Explain your meaning, please. _____

8. The wind whistled down the chimney. _____

9. The heavy floods blocked traffic for miles. _____

10. Many leaves have dropped in our yard. _____

11. Inventions change our way of living. _____

12. Birmingham, England, attracts many tourists. _____

13. Dorothea Lange was a famous photographer. _____

14. Julio has a fine collection of coins. _____

15. Who invented the lightning rod? _____

16. We cooked our steaks over an open fire. _____

17. Madame Curie discovered radium. _____

18. Gene traveled through North America and South America. _____

19. Cole Porter composed "Night and Day." _____

20. Amelia Earhart was a famous pilot. _____

21. The tornado destroyed several stores. _____

22. Paul exercises every day. _____

23. We talked for hours. _____

24. Have you ever seen Plymouth Rock? _____

25. Abandoned campfires often cause great forest fires. _____

26. He is studying hard for the exam. _____

27. The United States bought Alaska in 1867. _____

> ■ **Voice** refers to the relation of a subject to the action expressed by the verb.
> ■ In the **active voice,** the subject does the action.
>   EXAMPLE: The club **made** these decorations.
> ■ In the **passive voice,** the subject is acted upon.
>   EXAMPLE: These decorations **were made** by the club.
> ■ Only transitive verbs can be used in the passive voice.

■ **Underline each verb. Then write active or passive.**

_____passive_____ 1. The phonograph <u>was invented</u> by Edison.

_____ 2. Tim hit a home run.

_____ 3. The bell was rung by the caretaker.

_____ 4. The football was thrown out of bounds.

_____ 5. Ricardo has bought some new fishing tackle.

_____ 6. The decision of the committee was announced yesterday.

_____ 7. Steve blamed Paul for making him late.

_____ 8. The first three people were selected for the job openings.

_____ 9. Carl typed the letter.

_____ 10. Angela quickly stated the reason for not attending.

_____ 11. Andrew flopped into the chair.

_____ 12. Many songs were written by Foster.

_____ 13. The police officer gave me a ticket.

_____ 14. Dr. Koneru held a press conference.

_____ 15. Rosa has bought a new car.

_____ 16. His heart was broken by the cruelty of his friends.

_____ 17. Senator Dale shook their hands.

_____ 18. The boat was carried to the landing.

_____ 19. The party was given for her birthday.

_____ 20. Pam wrote the winning essay.

> - A **gerund** is the present participle of a verb form ending in -ing that is used as a noun.
> - A gerund may be the subject, direct object, or object of a preposition.
>   EXAMPLES: **Exercising** is vital to good health. (subject)
>   Tanya enjoys **exercising.** (direct object)
>   I have thought of **exercising.** (object of preposition)

■ **Underline each gerund.**

1. We enjoy living on the farm.

2. Airplanes are used in fighting forest fires.

3. Landing an airplane requires skill.

4. Climbing Pikes Peak is quite an experience.

5. The moaning of the wind through the pines lulled me to sleep.

6. The dog's barking awakened everyone in the house.

7. Keeping his temper is difficult for John.

8. Sue objected to our hanging the picture in this room.

9. Laughing aloud is encouraged by the comedian.

10. Being treasurer of this club is a responsibility.

11. Making a speech makes me nervous.

12. Winning this game will place our soccer team first in the league.

13. It was my first attempt at pitching horseshoes.

14. Rapid eating will make digestion difficult.

15. Playing golf is a favorite pastime in many countries.

16. Planning a party requires much thought.

17. We have completed our packing for the trip to the mountains.

18. The howling of the dogs disturbed our sleep.

19. I am tired of doing this work.

20. We are fond of living here.

21. Native Americans once spent much time planting, hunting, and fishing.

22. Neat writing is important in school.

23. I enjoy skating on this pond.

24. Jason taught us the rules of boating.

25. Pressing the wrong button can be very dangerous.

26. Airplanes are used in the mapping of large areas.

27. Swimming in this lake is my favorite sport.

28. I enjoy driving a car.

> ■ An **infinitive** is the base form of the verb, commonly preceded by <u>to</u>.
> ■ An infinitive may be used as a noun, adverb, or adjective.
>   EXAMPLES: **To know** him is **to like** him. (noun) She came here **to study.** (adverb) That is the movie **to see.** (adjective)

■ **Underline each infinitive.**

1. I want <u>to go</u> home before it gets any colder.

2. We went to see the play while Emilio was here.

3. I prepared the salad to serve for lunch.

4. To shoot firecrackers in the city limits is against the law in some places.

5. I like to walk in the country.

6. They were taught to stand, to sit, to walk, and to dance gracefully.

7. Gradually people learned to use fire and to make tools.

8. I need to get a new coat.

9. We plan to make the trip in four hours.

10. Carol, are you too tired to clean the kitchen?

11. Jack, try to be on time in the morning.

12. Anthony plans to travel in Canada during August.

13. Who taught you to play golf?

14. We were taught to rise early.

15. We were hoping to see you at the reunion.

16. Pay one fee to enter the amusement park.

17. Jennifer, I forgot to mail your package.

18. To cook this turkey will require several hours.

19. The children ran to meet their friend.

20. We are learning to speak Spanish.

21. We are planning to exhibit our artwork next week.

22. To succeed as an artist was Rick's dream.

23. We went to see the parade.

24. We are ready to eat.

25. It was easy to see the reason for that actor's popularity.

26. The only way to have a friend is to be one.

27. Madame Curie was the only woman to receive the Nobel Prize a second time.

28. To score the most points is the object of the game.

29. We need to go grocery shopping.

30. Do you want to paint the fence on Saturday?

■ A **present** or **past participle** is a verb form that may be used as an adjective.

EXAMPLES: A **dripping** faucet can be a nuisance. **Wilted** flowers were removed from the vase.

■ **Underline each participle.**

1. We saw a running deer in the forest.

2. The chart showing sales figures is very helpful.

3. The scampering cat ran to the nearest tree.

4. A team of deep-sea divers discovered the hidden treasure.

5. We saw the thunderstorm advancing across the plains.

6. Biting insects hovered over our campsite at night.

7. His foot, struck by the falling timbers, was injured.

8. The whispering pines filled the air with their fresh scent.

9. People preparing for a career in aviation should master mathematics.

10. We drove slowly, enjoying every minute of the drive.

11. Onions are among the largest vegetable crops produced in the United States.

12. The truck, burdened with its load, traveled slowly over the rough road.

13. Jan, thinking about her new job, was very happy.

14. Several passengers injured in the wreck were brought to the local hospital.

15. That expanding city will soon be the largest one in the state.

16. The fire, fanned by the high winds, threatened the entire area.

17. The rude person, shoving others aside, went to see the manager.

18. The lake, frozen solidly, looked like a huge mirror.

19. The man playing the trombone is my brother.

20. The cleaned apartment was ready for new tenants.

21. Teasing children ran at Rip Van Winkle's heels.

22. Balloons lifting weather instruments are released daily by many weather stations.

23. The chirping bird flew from tree to tree.

24. The surviving pilot described the accident.

25. The dedicated artist worked patiently.

26. Homing pigeons were used in the experiment.

27. The whistling youngster skipped happily down the road.

28. Ironed shirts were stacked neatly at the cleaners.

29. Those standing near the fence should form a second line.

30. The child ran to his loving father, who comforted him.

> - The verb <u>lie</u> means "to recline" or "to occupy a certain place." It does not take an object.
>   EXAMPLE: The baby is **lying** in her crib.
> - The verb <u>lay</u> means "to place." It takes an object.
>   EXAMPLE: **Lay** the plates on the shelf.
> - The following are forms of lie and lay:
>
> | Present | Present Participle | Past | Past Participle |
> |---------|--------------------|------|-----------------|
> | lie | lying | lay | (have) lain |
> | lay | laying | laid | (have) laid |

A. Circle the correct word in parentheses to complete each sentence.

1. Canada (lays, lies) to the north of the United States.

2. (Lay, Lie) these books on the table.

3. My cat was (laying, lying) on the floor.

4. Stuart likes to (lay, lie) in the shade.

5. James (lay, laid) the morning paper by his plate.

6. She (lay, laid) the letter on the table.

7. I have (lain, laid) awake for hours the last two nights.

8. He is not able to (lay, lie) on his left side.

9. Carol (lay, laid) her book aside and went to the door.

10. Where (lies, lays) the land to which these ships are going?

11. The dogs had (laid, lain) under the porch all night.

12. I (lay, laid) a long time beside the swimming pool.

13. California (lays, lies) to the east of the Pacific Ocean.

B. Write four sentences, each with a different form of <u>lie</u>, and write four sentences, each with a different form of <u>lay</u>.

1. a. _____

   b. _____

   c. _____

   d. _____

2. a. _____

   b. _____

   c. _____

   d. _____

- The verb sit means "to take a resting position."
  EXAMPLE: Please **sit** in that chair.
- The verb set means "to place."
  EXAMPLE: **Set** the cups on the saucers.
- The verb learn means "to acquire knowledge."
  EXAMPLE: I want to **learn** how to tap dance.
- The verb teach means "to give knowledge to" or "to instruct."
  EXAMPLE: Please **teach** me to tap dance.

Present	Present Participle	Past	Past Participle
sit	sitting	sat	(have) sat
set	setting	set	(have) set
learn	learning	learned	(have) learned
teach	teaching	taught	(have) taught

■ **Circle the correct word in parentheses.**

1. Please (sit, set) this table on the patio.

2. My friend is (learning, teaching) us to swim this summer.

3. You should (learn, teach) to eat more slowly.

4. Where do you prefer to (sit, set)?

5. The little dog is always found (sitting, setting) by its owner.

6. Such an experience should (learn, teach) you a lesson.

7. In a theater I always like to (sit, set) near the aisle.

8. I (sat, set) in a reserved seat at the last game.

9. Let me (learn, teach) you a shorter way to do this.

10. Alberto, please (sit, set) down on the step.

11. If you (learn, teach) me how to play tennis, I'll try to (learn, teach) well.

12. With tired sighs, we (sat, set) down on the couch.

13. Andrew, have you (sit, set) out the plants?

14. Jerry, did you (learn, teach) your dog all these tricks?

15. We watched the workers as they (sat, set) stone upon stone.

16. Marcy has (learned, taught) me to water-ski.

17. You can (learn, teach) some animals more easily than others.

18. Mona, do you like to (sit, set) by the window?

19. The first-aid course has (learned, taught) me important procedures.

20. Who (learned, taught) you how to ride a bike?

21. Please (sit, set) these chairs on the rug.

22. Manuel has (sat, set) his work aside.

23. Claire is (learning, teaching) children how to sail in August.

24. All the students are (sitting, setting) quietly.

- A **pronoun** is a word used in place of a noun.
- A **personal pronoun** is chosen based on the way it is used in the sentence.
  A **subject pronoun** is used in the subject of a sentence and after a linking verb.
  EXAMPLES: **He** is a chemist. The chemist is **he**.
  An **object pronoun** is used after an action verb or a preposition.
  EXAMPLES: Jan gave **me** the gift. Jan gave the gift to **me**.
  A **possessive pronoun** is used to show ownership of something.
  EXAMPLES: The new car is **ours**. That is **our** car.

■ **Underline each pronoun.**

1. Brian, do you have my ticket to the play?

2. Just between you and me, I want to go with them.

3. Carol, will you help me carry our trunk?

4. May I go with you?

5. We saw him standing in line to go to a movie.

6. Just be sure to find Carol and me.

7. We will be ready when they come for us.

8. She sent this box of frozen steaks to Andrea and me.

9. She asked you and me to be on her bowling team.

10. We saw them go into the building on the corner.

11. Last week we sent flowers to our sick friend.

12. He must choose their dinner.

13. She is my English instructor.

14. They have never invited us to go with them.

15. The first-place winner is she.

16. Can he compete against you?

17. She made the dinner for us.

18. Liz and I are going on vacation in June.

19. Where is your umbrella?

20. Sharon gave me a book to read.

21. Do you know where our cottage is?

22. If I lend you my car, will you take care of it?

23. I gave him my word that we would visit her.

24. When they saw us fishing, Bob and Diane changed their clothes.

25. Your toes are peeking through your socks.

26. Marie showed us how to fasten her bike to our car.

Using *Its* and *It's*

> ■ It's is a contraction for "it is." EXAMPLE: **It's** a beautiful day.
> ■ Its is a personal pronoun. EXAMPLE: The dog hurt **its** leg.

A. Underline the correct word in each sentence.

1. Our town is proud of (its, it's) elected officials.

2. (Its, It's) time for the curtain to rise.

3. Tell me when (its, it's) time for that television program.

4. (Its, It's) a mile from our house to the grocery store.

5. I think (its, it's) too cold to walk.

6. (Its, It's) almost time for the show to start.

7. (Its, It's) noon already.

8. (Its, It's) time to give the puppy (its, it's) bath.

9. The cat is playing with (its, it's) toy.

10. (Its, It's) time for us to start home.

11. It looks like (its, it's) going to rain.

12. This dog has lost (its, it's) collar.

13. I think that bird has hurt (its, it's) wing.

14. I do believe (its, it's) getting colder.

15. The dog is looking for (its, it's) owner.

16. (Its, It's) a long and very interesting story.

17. Do you know (its, it's) color was green?

18. The pony shook (its, it's) head and ran to the stable.

19. Do you think (its, it's) too late to call?

20. The bear cub imitated (its, it's) mother.

B. Write three sentences of your own in which you use <u>its</u>.

1. _____

2. _____

3. _____

C. Write three sentences of your own in which you use <u>it's</u>.

1. _____

2. _____

3. _____

Demonstrative and Indefinite Pronouns

> - A **demonstrative pronoun** is used to point out a specific person or thing.
> - This and that are used in place of singular nouns. This refers to a person or thing nearby, and that refers to a person or thing farther away.
>   - EXAMPLES: **This** is mine. **That** is the right one.
> - These and those are used in place of plural nouns. These points to persons or things nearby, and those points to persons or things farther away.
>   - EXAMPLES: **These** are the best ones. **Those** don't look ripe.

A. Underline each demonstrative pronoun.

1. Those are the books I lost.

2. That is where Anne lives.

3. I'm not sure these are my scissors.

4. This is my pen; that is Pam's book.

5. I think those are interesting books.

6. Is that your first mistake?

7. This is Gretchen's timecard.

8. Give these to your friend.

9. These are Stephanie's shoes.

10. Please don't mention this.

11. I think those are just rumors.

12. Will this be our last chance?

13. Dave, those are your messages.

14. These are large peaches.

15. Sorry, that was my last piece.

16. Who told you that?

> - An **indefinite pronoun** does not refer to a specific person or thing.
>   - EXAMPLE: **Many** are called, but **few** are chosen.
> - The indefinite pronouns anybody, anyone, anything, each, everyone, everybody, everything, nobody, no one, nothing, one, somebody, someone, and something are singular. They take singular verbs.
>   - EXAMPLE: **Everyone is** ready.
> - The indefinite pronouns both, few, many, several, and some are plural. They take plural verbs.
>   - EXAMPLE: **Several are** ready.

B. Underline each indefinite pronoun.

1. Both worked hard.

2. Let each help decorate.

3. Several have called about the job.

4. Unfortunately, some never learn.

5. Everyone was delighted at our party.

6. I think someone forgot this sweater.

7. Some asked for pens.

8. He thinks that each is right.

9. Has anyone seen my wallet?

10. Will someone wash the dishes?

11. Both of the singers are here.

12. One is absent.

13. Each must carry a bag.

14. Some always succeed.

15. Did someone leave this lunch?

16. Everybody is to be here early.

> - An **antecedent** is the word to which a pronoun refers.
>   EXAMPLE: **Stars** are lovely when **they** shine.
> - A pronoun must agree with its antecedent in **gender (masculine, feminine,** or **neuter)** and **number (singular** or **plural).**
>   EXAMPLES: **Susan** helped **her** friend. The **people** went in **their** cars.
> - If the antecedent is an indefinite pronoun, it is correct to use a masculine pronoun. However, it is now common to use both a masculine and feminine pronoun.
>   EXAMPLES: **Someone** lost **his** dog **Someone** lost **his or her** dog.

■ **Underline the correct pronoun, and circle its antecedent.**

1. Everyone should work hard at (their, his or her) job.
2. Each of the children willingly did (his or her, their) share of the camp duties.
3. Sophia gave me (her, their) coat to wear.
4. I took (my, our) friend to the ceremony.
5. All members were asked to bring (his or her, their) contributions today.
6. The women have had (her, their) vacation.
7. Someone has left (her or his, their) automobile across the driveway.
8. If each does (his or her, their) best, our chorus will win.
9. Would you tell Joanne that (her, his) soup is ready?
10. Every woman did (her, their) best to make the program a success.
11. Never judge anyone entirely by (his or her, their) looks.
12. Each student should do (his or her, their) own work.
13. I lost (my, our) favorite earring at the dance.
14. Each woman takes (her, their) own equipment on the camping trip.
15. Each one has a right to (his or her, their) own opinion in this matter.
16. (His, Her) sense of humor is what I like best about Joseph.
17. Some man has left (his, their) raincoat.
18. The two waiters dropped (his, their) trays when they bumped into each other.
19. Has each student received (his or her, their) report card?
20. Every person is expected to do (her or his, their) best.
21. We knew that every man at the meeting expressed (his, their) opinion.
22. Every woman furnishes (her, their) own transportation.
23. Jeff and Tom found (his, their) cabin in the dark.
24. Cliff brings his dog every time (he, she) visits.
25. The bird was in (their, its) nest.
26. Mark read (his, her) final essay for me.

> ■ A **relative pronoun** is a pronoun that can introduce a subordinate clause. The relative pronouns are who, whom, whose (referring to persons); which (referring to things); and that (referring to persons or things).
> ■ A **subordinate clause**, when introduced by a relative pronoun, serves as an adjective. It modifies a word, or antecedent, in the main clause.
> EXAMPLES: Tom knows the author **whose** articles we read in class. The family for **whom** I work is from Canada. The movie **that** won the prize is playing.

■ **Underline each relative pronoun, and circle its antecedent.**

1. The (letter) that was published in our daily paper was very long.
2. It was Karen who sang the most difficult song.
3. Robert Burns, who wrote "My Heart's in the Highlands," was Scottish.
4. It was Sylvia who wanted Zach's address.
5. The shop that was filled with video games is going out of business.
6. My parents live in a New England farmhouse that was built many years ago.
7. This is the pearl that is so valuable.
8. The bridge, which is made of wood, was built two hundred years ago.
9. Did you see the animal that ran across the road?
10. Good roads have opened up many regions that were formerly impassable.
11. For our Thanksgiving dinner, we had a turkey that weighed twenty pounds.
12. This story, which was written by Eudora Welty, is most interesting.
13. Anna is a person whom you can trust.
14. We ate the delicious hamburgers that Andrew had prepared.
15. Food that is eaten in pleasant surroundings is usually digested easily.
16. This is the first painting that I did.
17. The sweater that you want is too expensive.
18. She is the one whom we watched at the track meet.
19. The only money that they spent was for food.
20. Your friend is one person who is inconsiderate.
21. A rare animal that lives in our city zoo was featured on the evening news.
22. Heather is one of the guests whom I invited.
23. Is this the file for which you've been searching?
24. Leonardo da Vinci is the artist whose work they most admire.
25. The science museum is an attraction that is visited by many tourists.
26. Charles Dickens is a writer whom I've read extensively.

Lesson 46

Using *Who/Whom*

> ■ Use who as a subject pronoun.   EXAMPLE: **Who** is your favorite rock star?
> ■ Use whom as an object pronoun.   EXAMPLE: **Whom** did Karen call?
> By rearranging the sentence (Karen did call **whom**?), you can see that
> whom follows the verb and functions as the object. It can also function
> as the object of a preposition.   EXAMPLE: For **whom** are you looking?

■ **Complete each sentence with who or whom.**

1. _____ told you about our plans?

2. _____ is our greatest living scientist?

3. _____ did Armando send for?

4. _____ are those women?

5. _____ is your instructor?

6. _____ is your friend?

7. To _____ is that package addressed?

8. For _____ shall I ask?

9. _____ do you think can take my place?

10. From _____ did you borrow that costume?

11. _____ have the people elected?

12. _____ does she look like?

13. With _____ do you plan to study?

14. _____ is the new employee?

15. _____ do I resemble, my mother or my father?

16. The person _____ I called is my sister.

17. For _____ is this letter?

18. _____ will we select?

19. _____ told us about Frank?

20. _____ did he call?

21. _____ sat next to me?

■ **Underline the correct pronoun.**

1. It was (I, me) who brought the telegram.

2. (He, Him) and (I, me) are friends.

3. She used a sentence (who, that) contained a clause.

4. Neither (he, him) nor (she, her) was to blame.

5. Megan, will you sit between Dana and (I, me)?

6. The person (who, which) taught us how to swim has moved.

7. (Who, Whom) do you want?

8. Between you and (I, me), I do not believe that rumor.

9. I was not the only person (who, whom) she helped.

10. Lupe, please let Carla and (I, me) go with you.

11. For (who, whom) did Joanne knit this sweater?

12. A misunderstanding arose between (she, her) and (I, me).

13. Did you and (she, her) speak to (he, him) about the meeting?

14. The doctor (who, which) examined the sick child was very gentle.

15. That is a fox, and (them, those) are coyotes.

16. Is that (she, her) in your car?

17. Calvin invited Zachary and (I, me) to go swimming.

18. Everyone will write (his or her, their) name.

19. Between you and (I, me), I am disappointed.

20. (Those, That) are my books.

21. Patricia chose you and (I, me).

22. Have you ever played tennis with Brenda and (he, him)?

23. (These, This) are very expensive.

24. It is (he, him) who always plans our refreshments.

25. Were Charles and (he, him) ill yesterday?

26. (Those, That) are the singers we want to hear.

27. Our boss will tell Andy and (I, me).

28. Was it (he, him) who won the prize?

29. The person (who, whom) we met comes from Brazil.

30. Both want (his or her, their) papers.

31. (Who, Whom) walked three miles this morning?

32. Was it (she, her) who called this morning?

33. No one should comb (his or her, their) hair in public.

34. I thanked the woman (who, whom) helped me.

- An **adjective** is a word that modifies a noun or a pronoun.
  EXAMPLE: He has **red** hair.
- A **descriptive adjective** usually tells **what kind, which one,** or **how many.**
  EXAMPLES: **dreary** weather, **this** camera, **two** tickets
- A **proper adjective** is an adjective that is formed from a proper noun. It always begins with a capital letter.
  EXAMPLES: **Swedish** history, **Mexican** food
- The articles <u>a</u>, <u>an</u>, and <u>the</u> are called **limiting adjectives.**

A. Underline each adjective.

1. The old delicatessen sells fabulous Greek pastries.

2. The little dog is a very affectionate pet.

3. The weary traveler lay down upon the soft, green turf.

4. The storm was accompanied with a magnificent display of vivid lightning.

5. Every motorist should have good eyes, good ears, and good judgment.

6. Every child in the United States knows about the famous ride of Paul Revere.

7. Fleecy, white clouds were floating overhead.

8. On every side were lofty peaks.

9. We have many clear, bright days in December.

10. Washington was a person of courage and honor.

11. The beautiful memorial fountain was placed near the main entrance of the city park.

12. Cautious movements are required in dangerous areas.

13. Alaska, with its fertile soil, extensive forests, and valuable mines, is a great state.

14. He has a massive head, a broad, deep brow, and large, black eyes.

15. The rain dashed against the windows with a dreary sound.

16. Exercise should be a part of your daily routine.

17. The main street is bordered by stately elms.

18. Show a friendly attitude toward your classmates.

19. The second seat in the fourth row is broken.

20. The bright, colorful leaves of the maple make a wonderful sight in autumn.

21. The old, dusty books were donated to the library.

22. Yellow and green parrots talked to the curious children.

23. The steaming blueberry pie was set on the table.

24. An elegant woman stepped out of the black limousine.

25. Can you hear the chirping baby robins?

26. The salesperson waited on the first customer in line.

B. Form a proper adjective from each proper noun, and use it in a sentence.

1. Puerto Rico _____

2. Ireland _____

3. South America _____

4. Britain _____

5. France _____

6. Rome _____

7. Canada _____

8. England _____

9. Russia _____

C. Write three adjectives to describe each noun.

1. a friend _____ _____ _____

2. a TV program _____ _____ _____

3. a book _____ _____ _____

4. a sunset _____ _____ _____

5. a conversation _____ _____ _____

6. a soldier _____ _____ _____

7. a party _____ _____ _____

8. a pet _____ _____ _____

9. a child _____ _____ _____

10. a tree _____ _____ _____

D. Write two adjectives that could be substituted for the following common adjectives.

1. pretty _____ _____

2. little _____ _____

3. smart _____ _____

4. big _____ _____

5. nice _____ _____

6. good _____ _____

Demonstrative Adjectives

> - A **demonstrative adjective** is one that points out a specific person or thing.
> - This and that modify singular nouns. This points to a person or thing nearby, and that points to a person or thing farther away.
>   EXAMPLES: **This** pasta is delicious! **That** road will lead us to town.
> - These and those describe plural nouns. These points to people or things nearby, and those points to people or things farther away.
>   EXAMPLES: **These** sunglasses are very stylish. **Those** plants grow well in shady areas.
> - The word them is a pronoun. Never use it to describe a noun.

■ **Underline the correct word.**

1. Please hand me one of (those, them) pencils.

2. Who are (those, them) people?

3. Was your report made from (these, them) articles?

4. Have you heard (those, them) harmonica players?

5. (These, Them) ten problems are very difficult.

6. I do not like (that, those) loud music.

7. I like (this, these) kind of soft lead pencil.

8. (Those, Them) shoes are too small for you.

9. Where did you buy (those, them) cantaloupes?

10. Most people like (that, those) kind of mystery story.

11. Please look carefully for (those, them) receipts.

12. Sylvia, please take your brother (these, them) books.

13. (Those, Them) advertisements are very confusing.

14. (Those, Them) buildings are not open to the public.

15. Where did you find (that, those) uniform?

16. Please seat (these, them) guests.

17. Rich lives in (this, these) building.

18. (Those, Them) actors were exceptionally convincing in their roles.

19. Kelly, I sent you (that, these) brochure you requested.

20. Did you see (this, those) new outfits in the store?

21. Mark and Melissa painted (this, these) scenery.

22. (Those, Them) computer programs have been quite helpful.

23. Anna, would you like to read (these, them) memos?

24. (This, These) pair of sandals feels comfortable.

25. Is (that, those) the correct phone number?

- An adjective has three degrees of comparison: **positive, comparative,** and **superlative.**
- The simple form of an adjective is called the **positive** degree.
    EXAMPLE: Cornell is **happy.**
- When two people or things are being compared, the **comparative** degree is used.
    EXAMPLE: Cornell is **happier** than Katya.
- When three or more people or things are being compared, the **superlative** degree is used.
    EXAMPLE: Cornell is the **happiest** person I know.
- For all adjectives of one syllable and a few adjectives of two syllables, add -er to form the comparative degree and -est to form the superlative degree.
    EXAMPLE: tall—taller—tallest
- For some adjectives of two syllables, and all adjectives of three or more syllables, use more or less to form the comparative and most or least to form the superlative.
    EXAMPLES: He is **more** educated than I remember. That is the **most** beautiful horse on the farm. Yoko is **less** active than Mason. Brooke is the **least** active of all.
- Some adjectives have irregular comparisons.
    EXAMPLES: good, better, best   bad, worse, worst

A. Write the comparative and superlative forms of each adjective.

POSITIVE	COMPARATIVE	SUPERLATIVE
1. gentle		
2. helpful		
3. difficult		
4. troublesome		
5. high		
6. delicious		
7. intelligent		
8. soft		

B. Complete each sentence, using the correct degree of comparison for each adjective in parentheses.

1. (difficult)   This is the _____ problem I have ever faced.

2. (lovely)   A rose is _____ than its thorns.

3. (agreeable)   Ann is _____ in the morning than in the evening.

Adverbs

> - An **adverb** is a word that modifies a verb, an adjective, or another adverb.
>   EXAMPLES: Kevin spoke **casually**. Carmen's attitude is **very** positive.
>   We did the job **too** carelessly.
> - An adverb usually tells **how, when, where, to what extent,** or **how often.**
> - Many adverbs end in -ly.

■ **Underline each adverb in the sentences below.**

1. Preventive medicine has advanced rapidly.

2. The surface of the lake is very quiet.

3. Slowly and surely the tortoise won the race.

4. Afterward the child slept soundly.

5. Tom Sawyer's fence was carefully and thoroughly whitewashed.

6. The horse ran gracefully through the woods.

7. Slowly but steadily the river rose.

8. Jane, you read too rapidly.

9. Liz always dresses stylishly and neatly.

10. The driver turned quickly and abruptly.

11. Was the firefighter seriously injured?

12. Cynthia was extremely cautious as she moved slowly away from the danger.

13. Always try to speak correctly and clearly.

14. The assistant typed rapidly.

15. She came in very quietly.

16. Julio worked patiently and carefully.

17. We searched everywhere.

18. Our holidays passed too quickly.

19. The giant airplane landed gently.

20. We looked here, there, and everywhere for Sue's lost ring.

21. Come here immediately!

22. The flags were waving gaily everywhere.

23. Slowly the long freight train climbed the steep grade.

24. Overhead the stars twinkled brightly.

25. Wash your hands thoroughly before eating.

26. Scott caught the ball and speedily passed it to his teammate.

27. Carefully check every belt and hose in the car.

28. They were quite late.

29. He sees too many movies.

- An **adverb** has three degrees of comparison: **positive, comparative,** and **superlative.**
- The simple form of the adverb is called the **positive** degree.
    EXAMPLE: Alex worked **hard** on his project.
- When two actions are being compared, the **comparative** degree is used.
    EXAMPLE: Alex worked **harder** than Justin.
- When three or more actions are being compared, the **superlative** degree is used.
    EXAMPLE: Alex worked the **hardest** of all.
- Use -er to form the comparative degree, and use -est to form the superlative degree of one-syllable adverbs.
- Use more and most with longer adverbs and with adverbs that end in ly.
    EXAMPLE: Karen finished **more quickly** than Sally. Sally works the **most carefully** of the two.
- Some adverbs have irregular comparative and superlative degrees.
    EXAMPLES: well, better, best   badly, worse, worst

A. Write the comparative and superlative form of each adverb.

POSITIVE	COMPARATIVE	SUPERLATIVE
1. fast		
2. carefully		
3. quietly		
4. slow		
5. frequently		
6. proudly		
7. evenly		
8. long		

B. Complete each sentence using the correct degree of comparison for each adverb in parentheses. Some of the forms are irregular.

1. (seriously) Does Angela take her job _____ than Beth?

2. (high) Which of the kites flew _____ ?

3. (thoroughly) Who cleaned his plate _____ , Juan or Bruce?

4. (badly) This is the _____ I've ever done on a test.

5. (diligently) Carl works _____ than Mario!

6. (well) Lisa skis the _____ of everyone in her family.

■ **Underline the correct word.**

1. Always drive very (careful, carefully).

2. The lake seems (calm, calmly) today.

3. The storm raged (furious, furiously).

4. The dog waited (patient, patiently) for its owner.

5. Nicole's letters are always (cheerful, cheerfully) written.

6. Although our team played (good, well), we lost the game.

7. Always answer your mail (prompt, promptly).

8. James speaks (respectful, respectfully) to everyone.

9. Tara is (happy, happily) with her new work.

10. Write this address (legible, legibly).

11. The time passed (slow, slowly).

12. The robin chirped (happy, happily) from its nest.

13. We were (sure, surely) glad to hear from him.

14. Rebecca tries to do her work (good, well).

15. I think Brenda will (easy, easily) win that contest.

16. We had to talk (loud, loudly) to be heard.

17. Yesterday the sun shone (bright, brightly) all day.

18. He says he sleeps (good, well) every night.

19. The elevator went up (quick, quickly) to the top floor.

20. The storm began very (sudden, suddenly).

21. You did react very (cautious, cautiously).

22. Every student should do this work (accurate, accurately).

23. Eric rode his bike (furious, furiously) to get home on time.

24. The paint on the house is (new, newly).

25. The mist fell (steady, steadily) all evening.

26. The river looked (beautiful, beautifully) in the moonlight.

27. The salesperson always answers questions (courteous, courteously).

28. He always does (good, well) when selling that product.

29. Ryan can swim (good, well).

30. I was (real, really) excited about going to San Francisco.

31. I think he talks (foolish, foolishly).

32. It seems (foolish, foolishly) to me.

33. That bell rang too (loud, loudly) for this small room.

34. Our grass seems to grow very (rapid, rapidly).

Prepositions and Prepositional Phrases

> - A **preposition** is a word that shows the relationship of a noun or a pronoun to another word in the sentence.
>   EXAMPLES: I saw her coming **around** the **corner**.
>   She placed the present **on** the **chair**.
> - These are some commonly used prepositions:
>
> | about | against | at | between | from | of | through | until |
> |-------|---------|----|---------|------|----|---------|-------|
> | above | along | before | by | in | off | to | up |
> | across | among | behind | down | into | on | toward | upon |
> | after | around | beneath | for | near | over | under | with |
>
> - A **prepositional phrase** is a group of words that begins with a preposition and ends with a noun or pronoun.
>   EXAMPLE: We borrowed the lawn mower **from Ken**.
> - The noun or pronoun in the prepositional phrase is called the **object of the preposition**.
>   EXAMPLE: Megan hurried **down** the **stairs**.

- **Underline each prepositional phrase. Then circle each preposition.**

1. Salt Lake City, Utah's capital and largest city, was founded in 1847.

2. Sir Authur Conan Doyle is famous for creating the beloved detective Sherlock Holmes.

3. Standard time was adopted in the United States in 1884.

4. The geographic center of the United States is in Kansas.

5. The first safety lamp for miners was invented by Sir Humphrey Davy in 1816.

6. Many people of North Borneo live in houses that have been built on stilts in the Brunei River.

7. The children were charmed by the magician's tricks.

8. We visited the Royal Ontario Museum in Canada.

9. The first automobile show was held in New York City in 1900.

10. Self-government in the United States began in Jamestown in 1619.

11. The first street railway in the world was built in New York in 1832.

12. The inventor of the telephone was born in Scotland.

13. Who is the inventor of the printing press?

14. The shadowy outline of the giant skyscrapers loomed before us.

15. Our small boat bobbed in the waves.

16. The swivel chair was invented by Thomas Jefferson.

17. A raging storm fell upon the quiet valley.

18. I was lulled to sleep by the patter of the rain.

19. We found acorns beneath the tree.

20. That cow is standing in the middle of the road.

21. The child ran across the yard and around the tree.

22. A pine tree fell across the brook.

23. The first census of our country was taken in 1790.

24. Tons of violets are made into perfume each year.

25. The heart of a person pumps more than four quarts of blood in one minute.

26. The United States Patent Office was established in 1836.

27. One of the secrets of success is the wise use of leisure time.

28. The school board held its annual banquet at this hotel.

29. Duke Ellington was born in Washington, D.C.

30. Deposits of iron ore exist near the western end of the Great Lakes.

31. The bridge across this stream was destroyed by the recent storm.

32. Many herds of cattle once grazed on these plains.

33. The huddle in football was first used by a team from Georgia University in 1896.

34. The first skyscraper was built in Chicago.

35. Travelers of a century ago journeyed by stagecoach.

36. The tower of Delhi in India is a monument to the skill of its builders.

37. The quiet of the evening was broken by the rumbling of thunder.

38. The parachutist was injured when her parachute caught in a tree.

39. Aviation was born on a sand dune in North Carolina in 1903.

40. The first trolley car was installed in Richmond in 1885.

41. A box of rusty nails was in the corner of the garage.

42. Don't stand near the edge of that steep cliff.

43. The ground was covered with a deep snow.

44. Twenty cars were involved in the accident on the expressway.

45. The study of geography teaches us about the layout of other lands.

46. A thin column of smoke rose from the chimney of the cabin.

47. In the distance, we saw the top of the snow-capped peak.

48. Place the book upon the shelf.

49. At one time, Philadelphia was the capital of the United States.

50. The football sailed between the goal posts.

51. The report of the secretary was given at the beginning of the meeting.

52. A group of cheering fans waited at the entrance.

53. The hot air balloon drifted toward the ground.

54. Let's have our picnic beneath this huge tree.

55. In the glow of the fading light, we drove along the road.

56. Emily lives near the new mall.

57. Look in the card catalog to see if this book is in the library.

58. The tour guide led us through the halls of the mansion.

59. The theater group is meeting to discuss its productions for next year.

Conjunctions

- A **conjunction** is a word used to join words or groups of words.
  EXAMPLE: Jenna **and** her sister are in Arizona.
- These are some commonly used conjunctions:

although	because	however	or	that	when	while
and	but	if	since	though	whereas	yet
as	for	nor	than	unless	whether	

- Some conjunctions are used in pairs. These include either . . .or, neither . . . nor, and not only . . . but also.

- **Underline each conjunction.**

1. He and I are friends.

2. David likes tennis, whereas Jim prefers running.

3. We had to wait since it was raining.

4. We left early, but we missed the train.

5. The show was not only long but also boring.

6. Neither the chairs nor the tables had been dusted.

7. Hail and sleet fell during the storm.

8. Neither Carmen nor Kara was able to attend the meeting.

9. I have neither time nor energy to waste.

10. Bowling and tennis are my favorite sports.

11. Either Dan or Don will bring a portable radio.

12. The people in the car and the people in the van exchanged greetings.

13. Neither cookies nor cake is on your diet.

14. Although I like to take photographs, I am not a good photographer.

15. Did you see Charles when he visited here?

16. We are packing our bags since our vacation trip begins tomorrow.

17. She cannot concentrate while you are making so much noise.

18. Unless you hurry, the party will be over before you arrive.

19. We enjoyed the visit although we were very tired.

20. Both mammals and birds are warm-blooded.

21. She is one performer who can both sing and dance.

22. Unless you have some objections, I will submit this report.

23. Neither dogs nor cats are allowed in this park.

24. April watered the plants while Luis mowed the lawn.

25. I will see you when you are feeling better.

26. Either Ms. Andretti or Ms. Garcia will teach that course.

27. We got here late because we lost our directions.

> ■ The **adverbs** <u>not</u>, <u>never</u>, <u>hardly</u>, scarcely, seldom, <u>none</u>, and <u>nothing</u> should not be used with a negative verb. One clause cannot properly contain two negatives.
>   EXAMPLES: There wasn't anything left in the refrigerator. (Correct)
>   There wasn't nothing left in the refrigerator. (Incorrect)

■ **Underline the correct word.**

1. We couldn't see (anything, nothing) through the fog.

2. The suspect wouldn't admit (anything, nothing).

3. I don't know (any, none) of the people on this bus.

4. Rosa couldn't do (anything, nothing) about changing the time of our program.

5. We didn't have (any, no) printed programs.

6. I don't want (any, no) cereal for breakfast this morning.

7. You must not speak to (anyone, no one) about our surprise party plans.

8. There isn't (any, no) ink in this pen.

9. Didn't you make (any, no) copies for the other people?

10. I haven't had (any, no) time to repair the lawn mower.

11. She hasn't said (anything, nothing) about her accident.

12. Hardly (anything, nothing) pleases him.

13. There aren't (any, no) pears in this supermarket.

14. There isn't (any, no) newspaper in that little town.

15. There wasn't (anybody, nobody) in the house.

16. Please don't ask him (any, no) questions.

17. I haven't solved (any, none) of my problems.

18. I haven't done (anything, nothing) to offend Greg.

19. We don't have (any, no) water pressure.

20. Our team wasn't (any, no) match for the opposing team.

21. I couldn't hear (anything, nothing) because of the airplane's noise.

22. The salesperson didn't have (any, no) samples on display.

23. I haven't (any, no) money with me.

24. Hasn't he cooked (any, none) of the pasta?

25. We haven't (any, no) more packages to wrap.

26. Wasn't there (anyone, no one) at home?

27. My dog has never harmed (anybody, nobody).

28. They seldom have (anyone, no one) absent from their meetings.

29. There weren't (any, no) clouds in the sky.

A. Write C or P above each underlined noun to show whether it is a common or proper noun. Then identify each common noun as concrete, collective, or abstract.

_____ **1.** Mayor Murayama has a great deal of integrity.

_____ **2.** The public recognizes Julia's singing talent.

_____ **3.** Her computer is exactly like Craig's.

_____ **4.** Jim's sensitivity to others makes him well-liked.

B. Complete each sentence with the plural form of the word in parentheses.

1. (woman) The _____ in the choir are rehearsing tonight.

2. (calf) We stopped at the side of the road to watch the

_____ grazing.

3. (porch) . I like old Victorian homes with enclosed _____.

4. (potato) Will you please put the _____ in the oven?

5. (sister-in-law) Gina has three _____.

C. Fill in each blank with the possessive form of the word in parentheses.

1. (children) Hoan's favorite author is appearing at the _____

bookstore.

2. (lawyers) Rachel is attending a _____ conference.

3. (candidate) Did you hear that _____ most recent speech?

4. (men) The basketball team is practicing in the _____ gym.

D. Underline each verb phrase.

1. I should have been more thoughtful.

2. Tom is designing a newsletter for our company.

3. Did you mop the floor?

4. Your package might arrive this week.

5. We will leave tomorrow morning.

6. Dave has washed the car.

7. Chris is paying the bills.

8. Lucy and I have opened the package.

E. Underline each verb. Then identify each as transitive or intransitive.

1. I enjoyed my visit to the art museum. _____

2. The strong winds howled. _____

3. We studied the videotape of the incident. _____

F. Fill in the blank with the correct form of the verb in parentheses.

1. (eat) She has already _____ breakfast.

2. (do) Some people have _____ strange things.

3. (come) Kamal _____ to the meeting late.

4. (draw) Andrew's performance _____ a standing ovation.

5. (speak) James has _____ to me about the problem.

G. Identify the mood of each underlined verb as indicative, subjunctive, or imperative.

1. <u>Show</u> us your new house. _____

2. Who <u>forgot</u> to turn on the porch light? _____

3. I'd be glad about it if I <u>were</u> you. _____

4. Juan <u>bought</u> a new car. _____

H. Identify each underlined word or words as a gerund, an infinitive, or a participle.

1. <u>Crumpled</u> newspapers covered the floor. _____

2. <u>Inviting</u> them to the same party was a mistake. _____

3. I would like <u>to learn</u> a foreign language. _____

4. <u>Shopping</u> for gifts takes a great deal of time. _____

5. We are ready <u>to go</u>. _____

I. Identify each underlined pronoun as a subject, an object, or a possessive pronoun.

1. <u>Our</u> families live hundreds of miles apart. _____

2. James sent <u>me</u> his new address. _____

3. <u>They</u> have moved three times in two years. _____

4. I received a package from <u>them</u> yesterday. _____

5. Laura and <u>I</u> are working on the problem. _____

J. Underline each adjective. Circle each adverb.

1. These trails can be extremely hazardous.

2. After the long hike, we felt weary.

3. The large jar was soon filled with fresh strawberries.

4. Although it was small, the suitcase was quite heavy.

5. With a graceful movement, the horse suddenly jumped across the stream.

6. We will need two volunteers immediately.

A. Read the following paragraphs.

Tibet, which is a remote land in south-central Asia, is often called the Roof of the World or Land of the Snows. Its mountains and plateaus are the highest in the world. The capital of Tibet, Lhasa, is 12,000 feet high.

Tibetans, who are sometimes called the hermit people, follow a simple way of life. They are a short and sturdy people and do heavy physical work. Some are nomads, herders who roam about in the northern uplands of the country. Once a year, the nomads come to the low regions to sell their products and to buy things that they need. They live in tents made of yak hair. A yak is about the size of a small ox and has long hair. Yaks are good companions to the nomads because they can live and work in the high altitudes.

B. Write two appositives from the paragraph above.

_____   _____

C. Write four relative pronouns and their antecedents.

1. _____ _____   3. _____ _____

2. _____ _____   4. _____ _____

D. Write three prepositional phrases.

1. _____

2. _____

3. _____

E. Write one superlative adjective.

_____

F. Write one indefinite pronoun.

_____

G. Write two intransitive verbs.

_____   _____

H. Write two infinitives.

_____   _____

I. Write two conjunctions.

_____   _____

J. Read the following paragraphs.

If you were to guess which people were the first to learn to write, would you guess the Egyptians? Experts believe thousands of years ago, around 3100 B.C., Egyptians first began writing. Much of their writing was done to record historical events. Later, writings were used on pyramids to ensure peace for the kings buried in them. The writings were in hieroglyphics, a system of writing based on pictures.

Egyptian pyramids are notable for a number of reasons. The oldest pyramid is called Saqqarah. It was built with hundreds of steps running up to the top and was the first building in the country made entirely of stone. It clearly shows how advanced the ancient Egyptian culture was, both artistically and mechanically.

Another incredible monument is the Great Sphinx—a half-lion, half-man stone structure built for King Khafre. Historians have been able to learn much about the ancient Egyptian people by studying these buildings and the materials in them. Fortunately, the climate in Egypt was dry, so the writings and artifacts were well-preserved.

K. Write a subjunctive verb from the paragraph above.

_____

L. Write two adverbs.

_____   _____

M. Write two passive verbs.

_____   _____

N. Write an appositive.

_____

O. Write two abstract nouns.

_____   _____

P. Write two concrete nouns.

_____   _____

Q. Write two conjunctions.

_____   _____

R. Write two prepositional phrases.

_____

_____

- **Capitalize** the first word of a sentence and of each line of poetry.
  EXAMPLES: Maria wrote a poem. It began as follows:
  One cold, starry night
  I saw the stars taking flight.
- Capitalize all proper nouns.
  EXAMPLES: Ellen Kennan, Uncle John, First Street, Spain, Virginia, White Mountains, New Year's Day, March, Niles High School, *Sea Voyager*
- Capitalize the first word of a quotation.
  EXAMPLE: Tonya said, "Everyone should learn a poem."
- Capitalize the first, last, and all important words in the titles of books, poems, stories, and songs.
  EXAMPLES: "Somewhere Over the Rainbow"; *The Call of the Wild*
- Capitalize all proper adjectives. A proper adjective is an adjective that is made from a proper noun.
  EXAMPLES: the French language, German food, American tourists

A. Circle each letter that should be capitalized. Write the capital letter above it.

1. henry wadsworth longfellow wove the history of america into his poems

   "evangeline" and "the courtship of miles standish."

2. "the midnight ride of paul revere" is another of longfellow's poems.

3. The british ship *titanic* sank on its first trip from england to the united states.

4. the first law course offered by an american college was taught by george wythe.

5. he taught many famous people, including thomas jefferson and james monroe.

6. The mississippi river flows through vicksburg, mississippi, and new orleans, louisiana.

7. "what time do the church bells ring?" asked amelia.

8. robert answered, "i believe they ring every half hour."

9. Many centuries ago, vikings lived in what is now known as norway, sweden, and denmark.

10. the song "the battle hymn of the republic" was written by julia ward howe.

11. Mr. james nelson lives in chicago, illinois.

12. he asked, "have you ever seen a waterfall?"

13. The president of the united states lives in the white house.

14. Last summer I visited a hopi reservation.

15. The sequoia national park is on the western slope of the sierra nevada mountains in california.

> - Capitalize a person's title when it comes before a name.
>   EXAMPLES: Doctor Lerner, Judge Kennedy, Governor Thompson
> - Capitalize abbreviations of titles.
>   EXAMPLES: Mr. J. D. Little, Dr. Simon, Pres. Lincoln

B. Circle each letter that should be capitalized. Write the capital letter above it.

1. mayor jones and senator small attended the awards banquet Friday night.

2. dr. fox is a veterinarian at the local animal hospital.

3. The invitation said to respond to ms. hilary johnson.

4. No one expected judge randall to rule in favor of the defendant.

5. We were disappointed that gov. dickson couldn't speak at graduation.

6. In his place will be senator christopher larson.

7. The speaker will be introduced by supt. adams.

8. Will miss alden be the new history instructor?

9. dr. tabor is a surgeon at Parkside Hospital.

10. His first patient was mr. william benton.

> - Capitalize abbreviations of days and months, parts of addresses, and titles of members of the armed forces. Also capitalize all letters in the abbreviations of states.
>   EXAMPLES: Fri.; Aug.; 267 N. Concord Ave.; Col. Fernando Gonzales; Hartford, CT; Athens, GA

C. Circle each letter that should be capitalized. Write the capital letter above it.

1. When is maj. hanson expected back from his trip overseas?

2. The garage sale is at 101 w. charles st.

3. Have you ever been to orlando, fl?

4. There is a house for sale at the corner of maple ave. and sunset st.

5. Everyone in our company has the first mon. off in september for Labor Day.

6. The highest award for service was given to gen. t. j. quint.

7. The letter from memphis, tn, took only two days to arrive.

8. Did you know that col. kravitz will be stationed in dover, nh?

9. His address will be 1611 falmouth harbor, dover, nh 03805.

> ■ Use a **period** at the end of a declarative sentence.
>   EXAMPLE: We are going to Mexico on our vacation.
> ■ Use a **question mark** at the end of an interrogative sentence.
>   EXAMPLE: Do you know whose picture is on the one-dollar bill?

A. Use a period or question mark to end each sentence below.

1. Does this road wind uphill all the way to Carol's house____

2. Los Angeles, Mexico City, and Rome have all been sites of the Olympic Games____

3. Were there really one hundred people standing in line at the theater____

4. Wisconsin raises hay, corn, and oats____

5. Pablo, Tom, Carlos, and Ling were nominated as candidates____

6. Whom did you see, Elizabeth____

7. Haydn, Mozart, Mendelssohn, and Beethoven composed symphonies____

8. Hummingbirds and barn swallows migrate____

9. Do you think that Napoleon was an able leader____

10. Does Louise live in Los Angeles, California____

11. Who wrote the Declaration of Independence____

12. We flew from Seattle, Washington, to Miami, Florida____

13. Roy Avery is a guest of Mr. and Mrs. Benson____

14. Anna, have you read "The Gift of the Magi" by O. Henry____

B. Add the correct end punctuation where needed in the paragraphs below.

Have you ever heard of Harriet Tubman and the Underground Railroad____ During the Civil War in the United States, Harriet Tubman, a former slave, helped more than three hundred slaves escape to freedom____ Tubman led slaves on the dangerous route of the Underground Railroad____ It was not actually a railroad but a series of secret homes and shelters that led through the South to the free North and Canada____ How dangerous was her work____ There were large rewards offered by slaveholders for her capture____ But Tubman was never caught____ She said proudly, "I never lost a passenger____" She was called the Moses of her people____

During the war, she worked as a spy for the Union army____ An excellent guide, she would lead soldiers into enemy camps____ She also served as a nurse and cook for the soldiers____ She was well respected among leading abolitionists of the time____ She was also a strong supporter of women's rights____

Do you know what she did after the war____ She settled in Auburn, New York, and took care of her parents and any other needy black person____ She was always low on money but never refused anyone____ Later, she set up a home for poor African Americans____

> ■ Use a **period** at the end of an imperative sentence.
>   EXAMPLE: Please answer the telephone.
> ■ Use an **exclamation point** at the end of an exclamatory sentence and after an interjection that shows strong feeling. If a command expresses great excitement, use an exclamation point at the end of the sentence.
>   EXAMPLES: Ouch! Follow that car! The ringing is so loud! My ears hurt!

C. Add periods or exclamation points where needed in each sentence below.

1. I love to hike in the mountains____

2. Just look at the view in the distance____

3. Be sure to wear the right kind of shoes____

4. Ouch____ My blister is killing me____

5. Talk quietly and walk softly____

6. Don't scare away the wildlife____

7. Look____ It's a bald eagle____

8. I can't believe how big it is____

9. Take a picture before it flies away____

10. Its wings are bigger than I had ever imagined____

11. It's one of the most breathtaking sights I've ever seen____

12. Oh, look this way____ Here comes another one____

13. This is the luckiest day of my life____

14. Sit down on that tree stump____

15. Pick another place to sit____

D. Add the correct end punctuation where needed in the paragraphs below.

Which animal do you think has been on Earth longer, the dog or the cat____ If you answered the cat, you're right____ About 5,000 years ago in Egypt, cats became accepted household pets____ That was a long time ago____ Cats were actually worshipped in ancient Egypt____

The different members of the cat family have certain things in common____ House cats and wild cats all walk on the tips of their toes____ Isn't that incredible____ Even though all cats don't like water, they can all swim____ Another thing that all cats have in common is a keen hunting ability____ Part of this is due to their eyesight____ They see well at night and in dim light____ Did you know that the cat is the only animal that purrs____ A cat uses its whiskers to feel____ Its sense of touch is located in its whiskers____ The coat of a cat can be long-haired or short-haired, solid-colored or striped____ Some cats even have spots____ Can you name any types of cats____

> ■ Use a **comma** between words or groups of words that are in a series.
>   EXAMPLE: Colorado, Canadian, Ohio, Mississippi, and Missouri are names of well-known American rivers.
> ■ Use a comma before a conjunction in a compound sentence.
>   EXAMPLE: Once the rivers were used mainly for transportation, but today they are used for recreation and industry.
> ■ Use a comma after a subordinate clause when it begins a sentence.
>   EXAMPLE: When I got to the theater, the movie had already begun.

A. Add commas where needed in the sentences below.

1. Anita Travis and José went to the tennis tournament.

2. Before they found their seats the first match had already begun.

3. It was a close game and they weren't disappointed by the final score.

4. They had come to cheer for Antonio Fergas and he was the winner.

5. Although his opponent was very good Fergas never missed returning a serve.

6. While they watched the match Anita clapped cheered and kept score.

7. Travis and José watched a number of different matches but Anita followed Fergas.

8. He was signing autographs and Anita was first in line.

9. Antonio asked her name signed a tennis ball and shook her hand.

10. Because they enjoyed the match so much Travis José and Anita made plans to come back for the final match the next day.

11. They planned to see the men's women's and doubles' finals.

12. Fergas won the entire tournament and he became the youngest champion in the history of the tournament.

> ■ Use a comma to set off a quotation from the rest of the sentence.
>   EXAMPLES: "We'd better leave early," said Travis.
>   Travis said, "We'd better leave early."
> ■ Use two commas to set off a divided quotation. Do not capitalize the first word of the second part of the quotation.
>   EXAMPLE: "We'd better leave," Travis said, "or we'll be stuck in traffic."

B. Add commas to the quotations below.

1. "The first match starts at 9:00 A.M." said Travis.

2. Anita asked "Do you want to get seats in the same section as yesterday?"

3. "That's fine with me" said José.

4. José said "Fergas's first match is in Court B."

5. "I'll bring the binoculars" said Anita "and you can bring the cooler."

> - Use a comma to set off the name of a person who is being addressed.
>   EXAMPLE: Philip, would you like to leave now?
> - Use a comma to set off words like <u>yes</u>, <u>no</u>, <u>well</u>, <u>oh</u>, <u>first</u>, <u>next</u>, and <u>finally</u> at the beginning of a sentence.
>   EXAMPLE: Well, we better get going.
> - Use a comma to set off an appositive.
>   EXAMPLE: Alan, Philip's brother, is a doctor in Saint Louis.

C. Add commas where needed in the sentences below.

1. Dr. Perillo a nutritionist is an expert on proper eating.

2. "Students it's important to eat a well-balanced diet," she said.

3. "Yes but how do we know what the right foods are?" asked one student.

4. "First you need to look carefully at your eating habits," said Dr. Perillo.

5. "Yes you will keep a journal of the foods you eat," she said.

6. "Dr. Perillo what do you mean by the right servings?" asked Emilio.

7. "Okay good question," she said.

8. "A serving Emilio is a certain amount of a food," said Dr. Perillo.

9. "Dave a cross-country runner will need more calories than a less active student," explained Dr. Perillo.

10. "Class remember to eat foods from the five basic food groups," she said.

D. Add commas where needed in the paragraphs below.

Our neighbor Patrick has fruit trees on his property. "Patrick what kinds of fruit do you grow?" I asked. "Well I grow peaches apricots pears and plums" he replied. "Wow! That's quite a variety" I said. Patrick's son Jonathan helps his dad care for the trees. "Oh it's constant work and care" Jonathan said "but the delicious results are worth the effort." After harvesting the fruit Jonathan's mother Allison cans the fruit for use throughout the year. She makes preserves and she gives them as gifts for special occasions. Allison sells some of her preserves to Chris Simon the owner of a local shop. People come from all over the county to buy Allison's preserves.

Jonathan's aunt Christina grows corn tomatoes beans and squash in her garden. Each year she selects her best vegetables and enters them in the fair. She has won blue ribbons medals and certificates for her vegetables. "Oh I just like being outside. That's why I enjoy gardening" Christina said. Christina's specialty squash-and-tomato bread is one of the most delicious breads I have ever tasted.

> ■ Use **quotation marks** to show the exact words of a speaker. Use a comma or another punctuation mark to separate the quotation from the rest of the sentence. A quotation may be placed at the beginning or at the end of a sentence. Begin the quote with a capital letter. Be sure to include all the speaker's words within the quotation marks.
>   EXAMPLES: "Let's go to the movie," said Sharon.
>   "What time," asked Mark, "does the movie begin?"

A. Add quotation marks and other punctuation where needed in the sentences below.

1. Mary, do you think this is Christine's pen asked Heather.

2. Heather said I don't know. It looks like the kind she uses.

3. Well, I think it's out of ink, Mary replied.

4. Have you seen Barbara's car? asked Sandy.

5. No said Beth, I haven't gotten over to her apartment this week.

6. Sandy said It sure is pretty. I can't wait to ride in it.

7. I can't believe how late it is exclaimed Alan.

8. Paul asked Where are you going on vacation this summer?

9. My brother and I are visiting our parents in Maine said Peter.

10. Tell me, Alison said how many cats do you have?

11. Alison said The last time we counted, there were four.

12. Will you be taking the bus home asked James or do you need a ride?

> ■ Use an **apostrophe** in a contraction to show where a letter or letters have been taken out.
>   EXAMPLE: **Let's** go to the store. I **can't** go until tomorrow.
> ■ Use an apostrophe to form a possessive noun. Add -'s to most singular nouns. Add -' to most plural nouns. Add -'s to a few nouns that have irregular plurals.
>   EXAMPLES: **Maria's** sons are musicians. The **sons'** voices are magnificent. They sing in a **children's** choir.

B. Write the words in which an apostrophe has been left out. Insert apostrophes where they are needed.

1. Im sorry I cant make it to the concert. _____ _____

2. I cant go until Beths project is completed. _____ _____

3. Ill need two nights notice. _____ _____

4. Ive heard that the bandleaders favorite piece will be played last. _____

5. Isnt it one of Cole Porters songs? _____ _____

Lesson 61 — Using Colons and Semicolons

> ■ Use a **colon** after the greeting in a business letter.
>   EXAMPLES: Dear Mrs. Miller: Dear Sirs:
> ■ Use a colon between the hour and the minutes when writing the time.
>   EXAMPLES: 11:45   3:30   9:10
> ■ Use a colon to introduce a list.
>   EXAMPLE: The shopping cart contained the following items: milk, eggs, crackers, apples, soap, and paper towels.

A. Add colons where needed in the sentences below.

1. At 9 1 0 this morning, we'll be leaving for the natural history museum.

2. Please bring the following materials with you pencils, paper, erasers, and a notebook.

3. The bus will be back at 4 0 0 to pick us up.

4. The special exhibit on birds contains the following types prehistoric birds, sea birds, and domestic birds.

5. The letter we wrote to the museum began "Dear Sir Please let us know when the special exhibition on penguins will be shown at your museum."

6. He told us that we could find out more about the following kinds of penguins the Emperor, the Adélie, and the Magellan.

7. We were afraid there would be so much to see that we wouldn't be ready to leave at 3 3 0 when the museum closed.

> ■ Use a **semicolon** between the clauses of a compound sentence that are closely related but not connected by a conjunction. Do not capitalize the word after a semicolon.
>   EXAMPLE: Hummingbirds and barn swallows migrate; most sparrows live in one place all year.

B. Rewrite each sentence below, adding semicolons where needed.

1. Colleen is a clever teacher she is also an inspiring one.

_____

2. Her lectures are interesting they are full of information.

_____

3. She has a college degree in history world history is her specialty.

_____

4. She begins her classes by answering questions she ends them by asking questions.

_____

> ■ Use a **hyphen** between the parts of some compound words.
>   EXAMPLE: poverty-stricken   sixty-three   two-thirds
>   part-time   able-bodied   brother-in-law
>   hard-boiled   short-term   red-hot
> ■ Use a hyphen to separate the syllables of a word that is carried over from one line to the next.
>   EXAMPLE: So many things were going on at once that no one could possibly guess how the play would end.

A. Add hyphens where needed in the sentences below.

1. The director told us that there would be room for only two busloads, or eighty four people.

2. The play was going to be in an old fashioned theater.

3. Between acts the theater was completely dark, but the orchestra con tinued to play anyway.

4. The theater was so small that there were seats for only ninety two people.

5. The vice president was played by Alan Lowe.

> ■ Use a **dash** to set off words that interrupt the main thought of a sentence or to show a sudden change of thought.
>   EXAMPLES: We were surprised—even shocked—by the news.
>   It was Wednesday—no it was Friday—that I was sick.

B. Add dashes where needed in the sentences below.

1. There was a loud boom what a fright from the back of the theater.

2. We all turned around I even jumped up to see what it was.

3. It was part of the play imagine that meant to add suspense.

4. I'd love to see the play again maybe next week and bring Andrea.

> ■ **Underline** the titles of books, plays, magazines, films, and television series.
>   EXAMPLE: We read Romeo and Juliet last term.
> ■ Underline foreign words and phrases.
>   EXAMPLE: "Adieu," said the French actor to his co-star.

C. In the sentences below, underline where needed.

1. We saw the movie Of Mice and Men after we had read the novel.

2. In Spanish, "Hasta la vista" means "See you later."

3. My favorite book is Little Women.

4. I took a copy of Life magazine out of the library.

Review

A. Circle each letter that should be capitalized. Then add the correct end punctuation.

1. last thanksgiving we spent the holiday at my aunt's house in florida____

2. it was wonderful to be warm in november____

3. we visited the riverdale gardens, sea world, and the ringling museum____

4. one day, we went to see the ship *ocean dream*____

5. the boat's captain, mr. harvey land, took us on a tour____

6. he asked if any of us had been to crystal island____

7. when we answered no, he said he'd take us there on friday____

8. after that journey, I read *seafaring around the world*____

B. Add punctuation where needed in the sentences below.

1. We saw twenty four kinds of fish off the coast of Florida said Paul.

2. Did you snorkel asked Marie or did you stay on the ship?

3. Paul answered We began to snorkel in the shallow water at 2 0 0.

4. The captains first mate Jake is an experienced diver.

5. He offered to give us lessons said Paul.

6. What would he teach you asked Andrew.

7. Hed teach us said Paul how to approach the fish without scaring them away.

8. That must be great exclaimed Marie.

9. Yes I cant wait to learn said Paul.

10. Paul said I think hed be a fine teacher I know hes a great swimmer.

C. Punctuate the letter below. Then circle each letter that should be capitalized.

> 1200 s. clarke st
>
> chicago, il 60202
>
> june 10, 2006

Dear mr anderson,

    i cant tell you how much we appreciated the time you spent with us in florida____ it was the greatest trip ever____ because of our trip my sister and I plan to take introduction to oceanography at the seaworld institute here in chicago____ the course is offered to people of all ages at the alcott aquarium____ dont you think its funny that chicago has the seaworld institute and we arent even near the ocean____ the closest thing we have is lake michigan____ thanks again for all your help and time____

> Sincerely,
>
> paul mendoza

D. Rewrite the letter below. Capitalize necessary letters, and add needed punctuation.

1907 e adams blvd

phoenix az 94733

aug 18 2006

dear kmol radio

    i listened with interest to peter katz and filipa guerra on your 1000 show talk about town last friday night____ though i tried to call in the lines were always busy____ i thought id try writing it will at least make me feel better____

    i really couldnt believe my own ears____ what in the world do those two have in common with the public in general____ mr katz said hed never had to work a day in his life____ ms guerra said shed never been out of the state of new mexico____ well most of the people in arizona have to work____ many have come from another state____ neither of them has the right to tell working class people how to live____ my suggestions are these take a survey show it to your guests and demand an on air apology from them____

    by the way i have long wondered what kmol your call letters stand for if anything____ would you please answer that sometime on the air____ thanks for your time____

yours truly

erica mallet

_____

_____

_____

_____

_____

_____

_____

_____

_____

_____

_____

_____

Using What You've Learned

A. Add punctuation where needed in the paragraphs below. Circle each letter that should be capitalized. Be sure to underline book titles.

have you ever heard the story called "the dog and his bone"___ there once was a dog that had a new bone___ this is a great bone said the dog to himself___ the dog decided to take a walk and carried the bone proudly in its mouth___ he went down a dirt road and over a bridge___ as he was crossing the bridge he looked down into the river___ wow said the dog look at that big bone in the water___ the dog thought to himself id rather have that bone than the one i have right now___ can you guess what happened next___ well the dog opened his mouth and dropped the bone a foolish thing to do into the river___ when the splash of the bone hitting the water stopped the dog looked for the bigger bone___ however he didnt see it anymore___ what he did see was his old bone sinking to the bottom of the river___

_____

there is an incredible man scott targot who lives in my town___ his nickname is the ironman___ people call him ironman targot because he has won several triathlons___ do you know what a triathlon is___ some people consider it the ultimate sports contest___ athletes have to swim for 2.4 miles ride a bike for 112 miles and run for 26.2 miles___ just one of those alone is a lot of work___ scott will train from february to august in preparation for a triathlon in hawaii___ scott says i wouldnt want to be doing anything else with my time___ each day during training he gets up at 7 0 0 loosens up for a half hour then runs from 7 3 0 to 8 3 0___ after he cools down a little he takes a 20 mile bike ride___ at the end of the ride he swims for an hour and a half___ yes i get tired he says but i usually feel refreshed after swimming___ last he lifts light weights and takes a break to do some reading___ his favorite book is you can do it___

a triathlon is supposed to be completed in less than seventeen hours___ the record is less than half that time___ thats my goal says scott___ hes still trying to break 14 hours and ten minutes___ scotts usually one of the top finishers___

B. Write a sentence to illustrate each use of punctuation.

1. Comma   (three uses)

_____

_____

_____

2. Quotation mark   (two uses)

_____

_____

3. Apostrophe   (two uses)

_____

_____

4. Colon   (two uses)

_____

_____

5. Semicolon   (one use)

_____

_____

6. Hyphen   (two uses)

_____

_____

7. Dash   (one use)

_____

8. Underlining   (two uses)

_____

_____

C. Write a short paragraph about someone you admire. Follow all capitalization and punctuation rules.

_____

_____

_____

_____

- Every sentence has a base consisting of a simple subject and a simple predicate.
  EXAMPLE: <u>People</u> <u>applied</u>.
- Expand the meaning of a sentence by adding adjectives, adverbs, and prepositional phrases to the sentence base.
  EXAMPLE: **Several** people applied **at the technical institute last week.**

A. Expand the meaning of each sentence base below by adding adjectives, adverbs, and prepositional phrases. Write your expanded sentence.

1. (Visitors toured.) _____

2. (Machines roared.) _____

3. (People lifted.) _____

4. (Work stopped.) _____

5. (Buzzer sounded.) _____

B. Imagine two different scenes for each sentence base below. Write an expanded sentence to describe each scene you imagine.

1. (Day began.) **a.** _____

   b. _____

2. (Workers operated.) **a.** _____

   b. _____

3. (Supervisor explained.) **a.** _____

   b. _____

4. (Shipment arrived.) **a.** _____

   b. _____

5. (People unpacked.) **a.** _____

   b. _____

6. (Automobiles appeared.) **a.** _____

   b. _____

7. (Friend cooked.) **a.** _____

   b. _____

Writing Paragraphs

> ■ A **paragraph** is a group of sentences about one **main idea.** All the
> sentences in a paragraph relate to the main idea.
> ■ The first sentence in a paragraph is always indented.
> EXAMPLE:
> People work for a variety of reasons. One of the most important reasons
> people work is to earn money to buy goods and services they need.
> Work can also provide enjoyment or lead to achieving personal goals.

A. In each paragraph below, cross out the sentence that is not related to the main idea of the paragraph. Then write a new sentence that is related.

1. Bob and Todd have been friends since the day Bob's family first moved into the neighborhood. The boys were in the same class in both kindergarten and first grade. A few years later, they joined Scouts and worked together to earn merit badges. Bob's dad is an experienced carpenter. In junior high school, Bob was a star pitcher, while Todd led their team in batting.

_____

2. Rita's first job was at the swimming pool. Because she was a good swimmer and had passed a lifesaving course, she was asked to demonstrate swimming strokes during swimming instruction. She was not old enough to be an instructor. Sometimes she got jobs baby-sitting for families with children in the swimming program.

_____

B. Choose one of the topics below, and write a paragraph of three or four sentences that are related to it.

    a. Your first job   **c.** The job you'd most like to have
    b. The job everyone wants   **d.** Jobs in your community

_____

_____

_____

_____

_____

_____

_____

_____

_____

> ■ The **topic sentence** states the main idea of a paragraph. It is often placed at the beginning of a paragraph.
>
> EXAMPLE:
> Young people can learn various skills by working in a fast-food restaurant. They can learn how to use machines to cook food in a uniform way, how to handle money, and how to work with customers and with other employees.

A. Underline the topic sentence in each paragraph below.

1. Working in a fast-food restaurant is a good first job for young people. The hours are flexible. No previous experience is needed. The work is not hard.

2. A popular ice cream parlor in our town hires young people. Some work serving customers. Some work making special desserts. Others do cleanup and light maintenance.

3. Computers are used in fast-food restaurants. The cash register has a computer that totals purchase prices and computes change. Ovens and deep fryers have computers that regulate cooking temperatures.

B. Write a topic sentence for each group of related sentences.

1. Working may conflict with other activities. There may not be enough time for you to complete housework. You may miss out on having fun with friends.

Topic Sentence: _____

2. Kate manages the kitchen, plans the menus, and orders all the food. Jesse supervises the dining room. Jesse's sister does the bookkeeping for the restaurant. On weekends, my brother and I help clear the tables.

Topic Sentence: _____

3. The dining room was decorated with advertisements from the Fifties. The band played only music from the Fifties, and the waiters and waitresses all wore black slacks and bright pink bow ties.

Topic Sentence: _____

C. Write a topic sentence for one of the topics below.

    a. The best restaurant I've ever gone to   **c.** The job of waiter
    b. Restaurants in our town   **d.** The worst meal I've ever eaten

_____

_____

> ■ The idea expressed in a topic sentence can be developed with sentences containing **supporting details**. Details can include facts, examples, and reasons.

A. Circle the topic sentence, and underline four supporting details in the paragraph below.

In almost every professional sport, there are far more applicants than available jobs. Consider professional football. Every season, several hundred players are selected by thirty-two professional football teams. Of those chosen, only about ten percent are actually signed by a professional team. Furthermore, this number shrinks each year because team owners want smaller and smaller teams.

B. Answer the following questions about the supporting details you underlined.

1. What is one supporting detail that is a fact?

_____

_____

_____

2. What is a supporting detail that is a reason?

_____

_____

C. Read each topic sentence below, and write three supporting details for each.

1. People who want a career in sports could teach physical education.

_____

_____

_____

2. Professional sports teams employ people other than players.

_____

_____

_____

_____

Topic and Audience

> ■ The **topic** of a piece of writing is the subject written about.
> ■ The **audience** is the person or persons who will read what is written.
>   EXAMPLES: parents, teen-agers, school officials, engineers

A. Choose the most likely audience for each topic listed below.

        a. parents   **c.** job counselors
        b. high-school students   **d.** computer hobbyists

_____ **1.** future of personal computers   _____ **3.** jobs of the future

_____ **2.** benefits of a college education   _____ **4.** paying for college

B. Read the paragraph below, and answer the questions that follow.

    The evening was full of surprises. First, Brenda forgot to tell me she had five children. I had seen only two of them at the store with her. She also forgot to mention the cats—to which I am violently allergic. Also, I wasn't prepared to fix the children dinner. I wrongly assumed that Brenda would have fed them before I came. After getting everyone settled, I wondered if I should do the dishes. I figured that anyone with five children would appreciate having that job done.

1. What is the topic? _____

2. Name two possible audiences for the paragraph.

    _____

    _____

3. Explain why each audience might be interested.

    _____

    _____

    _____

    _____

C. Choose two topics that interest you. Write a topic sentence for a paragraph about each topic. Then name an audience for each paragraph.

1. Topic Sentence: _____

    Audience: _____

2. Topic Sentence: _____

    Audience: _____

Brainstorming

> ■ **Brainstorming** is a way to bring as many ideas to mind as you can. You can brainstorm by yourself or with others. As you brainstorm, write down your ideas. It is not necessary to write your ideas in sentence form.

A. Brainstorm about the things you would do if you were president of a major corporation. Write your ideas below.

1. _____

2. _____

3. _____

4. _____

B. Read the topics below. Choose one topic, and circle it. Then brainstorm about its advantages and disadvantages. Write down as many ideas as you can.

        a. volunteering   **d.** bicycle helmet laws

        b. eating healthy   **e.** automatic seat belts

        c. mediating disagreements   **f.** self-defense training

1. _____

2. _____

3. _____

4. _____

5. _____

6. _____

C. Now write a brief paragraph about the topic you chose in Exercise B that explains either the advantages or disadvantages of the topic.

_____

_____

_____

_____

_____

Outlining

- Before you write, organize your thoughts by making an **outline.** An outline consists of the title of the topic, headings for the main ideas, and subheadings for the supporting details.
- Main headings are listed after Roman numerals. Subheadings are listed after capital letters. Details are listed after Arabic numerals.

EXAMPLE:

Topic	Should Young People Be Paid for Doing Chores?
Main heading	I. Benefits to parents
Subheadings	A. Chores get done
	B. More leisure time
Main heading	II. Benefits to young people
Subheading	A. Learn useful skills
Details	1. Clean and do laundry
	2. Budget time
Subheading	B. Become responsible

- **Choose a topic that interests you. Then write an outline for that topic, using the example outline as a guide.**

_____

_____

_____

_____

_____

_____

_____

_____

_____

_____

_____

_____

_____

Lesson 70

Persuasive Composition

> ■ The writer of a **persuasive composition** tries to convince others to accept a personal opinion.

A. Read the following persuasive composition.

Everyone Should Learn to Use a Computer

Knowing how to use a computer is an essential skill for everyone who wants to succeed in today's world. One basic computer program that everyone should learn to use is the word processing program. Most types of writing are easily and professionally produced with a word processing program. For example, everyone must occasionally write a business letter. Using a computer allows you to arrange and rearrange information easily, making your writing more clear and accurate. Word processing programs can help you check your spelling and grammar. A computer makes it easy to correct mistakes.

Computers can be used for much more than word processing, however. Other areas of interest and opportunity in the field of computers are graphic design, programming, and creating new games. Jobs in the computer field are growing, and strong computer skills can serve you well now and into the future.

B. Answer the questions below.

1. List three facts the writer includes to persuade the reader.

_____

_____

_____

_____

_____

_____

2. List two reasons the writer includes in the composition.

_____

_____

_____

3. List one example the writer uses to support the topic.

_____

_____

_____

C. Choose one of the topic sentences below. Write a short paragraph in which you use facts to persuade your audience about the topic.

1. The driver and front-seat passenger in a car face various consequences if they don't wear seat belts.

2. More people should car-pool or use public transportation.

_____

_____

_____

_____

_____

D. Choose one of the topic sentences below. Write a short paragraph in which you use reasons to persuade your audience about the topic.

1. Wearing seat belts ensures all passengers of a safer ride.

2. The most important subject a person can learn about is _____ .

_____

_____

_____

_____

_____

E. Choose one of the topic sentences below. Write a short paragraph in which you use an example to persuade your audience about the topic.

1. I know someone who wore a seat belt and survived a serious collision.

2. _____ make the best pets.

_____

_____

_____

_____

_____

Revising and Proofreading

- **Revising** gives you a chance to rethink and review what you have written and to improve your writing. Revise by adding words and information, by deleting unneeded words and information, and by moving words, sentences, and paragraphs around.
- **Proofreading** has to do with checking spelling, punctuation, grammar, and capitalization. Use proofreader's marks to show changes needed.

Proofreader's Marks

Reverse the order.		Take something out.
Capitalize.	⊙ Add a period.	⑤ᴾ Correct spelling.
/ Make a small letter.	ᵛ Add quotation marks.	¶ Indent for new paragraph.
∧ Add a comma.	∧ Add something.	Move something.

A. Rewrite the paragraph below. Correct the errors by following the proofreader's marks.

¶ personal safety is one ^of the most important social issues today. Adults and ₵hildren are worried about staying safe in all these places ∧ their homes, their schools, and the places they go to have fun. one of the best things a person can do is to act with confidence and awarness. Confidents means "believing" and ∧ᵛawareness means ᵛseeing." Several studies have shone that people who act with confidence and awareness do not look like easy targets ∧ which is what criminals look for ⊙

_____

_____

_____

_____

_____

_____

_____

_____

_____

B. Read the paragraphs below. Use proofreader's marks to revise and proofread the paragraphs. Then write your revised paragraphs below.

When your outside your home, your body Language is important very. if you straigt stand, walk purposefully and pay attention to what is around you you will discourage Criminals because you appear strong and alert. along with confidence and awareness Another tool you can use all the time is your voice you can yell. Crimnals dont like to draw to attention themselves and they don't like to be seen. Yelling may sometimes be embarrassing, but your safety is more important than worrying about imbarrassment.

at home, its important to always keep your doors and windows locked you should never opent the door to someone you don't know. You don't have to be polite to somebody who may be trying to do you harm. This also applys to the telephone. If sombody you don't know calls and tries to keep you engaged in a conservation, just hang up. you don't have to be polite to somebody who is intruding in your life, especially if you don't know the person. always Keep your safety in mind and act in a way that discourages criminals from bothering you

_____

_____

_____

_____

_____

_____

_____

_____

_____

_____

_____

_____

_____

_____

A. Add adjectives, adverbs, and/or prepositional phrases to expand each sentence. Then write each expanded sentence.

1. (Producer recorded.) _____

2. (Notebook slipped.) _____

3. (Music started.) _____

4. (Crowd cheered.) _____

B. Write a topic sentence for the paragraph below. Name a possible audience for the paragraph.

> The job is not difficult as long as you are not afraid of dogs. Most dog owners have leashes, so the only materials you need are a notebook on which to write down your appointments and a pair of walking—or running, for some dogs—shoes. People who need to be away most of the day really appreciate the service and are willing to pay what you ask.

Topic Sentence: _____

Audience: _____

C. Read the topic sentence. Then underline the sentences that contain supporting details. Label each sentence fact, example, or reason, depending on the kind of supporting details it contains.

Topic Sentence: The widest variety of jobs is found in a hospital.

1. A hospital is a vital part of a community it serves.

   _____

2. A hospital employs technicians, secretaries, doctors, nurses, and business managers.

   _____

3. Many people are needed to carry out a hospital's many functions.

   _____

4. Our local hospital is the largest employer in our county.

   _____

5. A hospital's various facilities, such as its operating rooms, specialized departments, and food service, must work together efficiently.

   _____

6. I had a broken arm set in the emergency room last summer.

   _____

D. Write the items in outline form.

Topic: Pruning trees takes great skill.
Rake tree trash
Climb the tree
Choose and trim bad wood

Cleaning up
Haul trash
Brace your body firmly
Pruning the tree

_____

_____

_____

_____

_____

_____

_____

_____

_____

E. Read the persuasive paragraph. Then answer the questions below.

Everyone Should Vote

Elections are important, no matter what they are for. Voting in an election is democracy in action. Unless you take advantage of this privilege, you are letting a few people make your decisions for you. These decisions may be as small as who becomes class president or as important as who becomes the leader of an entire nation. Exercise your rights and make your beliefs and wishes known—vote in every election you possibly can.

1. What is one reason the writer gives for everyone to vote?

_____

2. What is one example the writer gives for the importance of voting?

_____

F. Read the paragraph below. Use proofreader's marks to revise and proofread the paragraph. Then write your revised paragraph below.

Artists choose from his materials that already are in existents to create their works of art all materials have there

own qualities. artists must know the characteristicks of their chosen materyal. They must work with it and not

aginst it materials are shaped in many ways cutting melting, hammering, and wearving are some of those waze.

_____

_____

_____

_____

A. Choose one of the topic sentences below. Write a short paragraph in which you use facts to persuade your audience about the topic.

1. Certain rules that apply to children do not apply to adults.
2. Community recycling programs benefit the environment.
3. A regular fitness program has many benefits.

_____

_____

_____

_____

_____

B. Choose one of the topic sentences below. Write a short paragraph in which you use reasons to persuade your audience about the topic.

1. Being a teacher is one of the most important jobs a person can have.
2. It is important to protect endangered animals from extinction.
3. High-school students should be required to take a driver-education course.

_____

_____

_____

_____

C. Choose one of the topic sentences below. Write a short paragraph in which you use an example to persuade your audience about the topic.

1. Dogs can be trained to be more than just pets.
2. A high-school diploma is necessary for obtaining many jobs.
3. You can learn a great deal about life from books.

_____

_____

_____

_____

_____

_____

D. Choose another topic from Exercises A, B, or C. Write a statement for a composition in which you wish to persuade your audience to consider your idea about the topic.

_____

E. Write a short outline of your ideas. Include main headings, subheadings, and details.

_____
_____
_____
_____
_____
_____
_____
_____
_____
_____

F. Write the first and second paragraphs of a short composition that persuades people about your idea. Use the outline you wrote as a guide. Then revise your paragraphs, and proofread them.

_____
_____
_____
_____
_____
_____
_____
_____
_____
_____
_____
_____

■ A **syllable** is a part of a word that is pronounced at one time. Dictionary
entry words are divided into syllables to show how they can be divided
at the end of a writing line.

■ A **hyphen** (-) is placed between syllables to separate them.
EXAMPLE: neigh-bor-hood

■ If a word has a beginning or ending syllable of only one letter, do not
divide it so that one letter stands alone.
EXAMPLES: a-bout   bur-y

A. Find each word in a dictionary. Then write each word with a hyphen between each syllable.

1. rummage _____

2. nevertheless _____

3. abominable _____

4. silhouette _____

5. biological _____

6. stationery _____

7. correspondence _____

8. character _____

9. enthusiasm _____

10. abandon _____

11. treacherous _____

12. effortless _____

13. romantic _____

14. nautical _____

15. accelerate _____

16. financial _____

17. significance _____

18. unimportant _____

19. commercial _____

20. ballerina _____

B. Write two ways in which each word may be divided at the end of a writing line.

1. imagination   imag-ination   imagina-tion

2. unexplainable _____   _____

3. tropical _____   _____

4. accomplishment _____   _____

5. encyclopedia _____   _____

6. librarian _____   _____

7. astronomic _____   _____

8. efficient _____   _____

9. cleanliness _____   _____

- Each dictionary entry word is followed by a respelling that shows how the word is **pronounced.**
- **Accent marks** (′) show which syllable or syllables are said with extra stress. A syllable pronounced with more stress than the others receives primary stress, shown by a heavy accent mark (′). A syllable said with lighter force receives secondary stress, shown by a lighter accent mark (′).

  EXAMPLE: con-grat-u-late (kən grach′ ə lāt′)
- A **pronunciation key** (shown below) explains the other symbols used in the respellings.

A. Use the pronunciation key to answer the questions.

1. Which word tells you how to pronounce the e in knee?

   _____

2. How many words are given for the symbol ə?

   _____

3. What symbol is used for the sound of the s in treasure?

   _____

> at; āpe; fär; câre; end; mē; it; īce; pîerce; hot; ōld; sông; fôrk; oil; out; up; ūse; rüle; pu̇ll; tûrn; chin; sing; shop; thin; **th**is; hw in white; zh in treasure. The symbol ə stands for the unstressed vowel sound in about, taken, pencil, lemon, and circus.

4. What symbol would be used for the sound of o in rob? _____

5. What symbol would be used for the sound of a in mark? _____

B. Use the pronunciation key to help you choose the correct word for each respelling. Underline the correct word.

1. (ōn)	own	an	on
2. (hēt)	heat	height	hate
3. (rod)	rode	road	rod
4. (tôk)	take	talk	took
5. (spēd)	speed	sped	spade
6. (wô′ tər)	waiter	whiter	water
7. (wāt)	wait	what	white
8. (spel)	spill	spoil	spell
9. (ān′ jəl)	angry	angel	angle
10. (must)	mist	must	most
11. (fēr)	fear	far	fir
12. (härd)	herd	hard	hoard
13. (frīt)	freight	fruit	fright
14. (sün)	sun	soon	sound

Dictionary: Definitions and Parts of Speech

- A dictionary lists the **definitions** of each entry word. Many words have more than one definition. In this case, the most commonly used definition is given first. Sometimes a definition is followed by a sentence showing a use of the entry word.
- A dictionary also tells the **part of speech** for each entry word. An abbreviation (shown below) stands for each part of speech. Some words may be used as more than one part of speech.

    EXAMPLE: **need** (nēd) *n.* **1.** the lack of something wanted or necessary. **2.** something wanted or necessary: *What are your basic needs for the camping trip? -v.* to require.

- **Use the dictionary samples below to answer the questions.**

pop-u-lar (pop′ yə lər) *adj.* **1.** pleasing to many people. **2.** having many friends: *Angela was voted the most popular girl in her class.* **3.** accepted by the general public: *The idea that pencils contain lead is a popular error.*

por-poise (pôr′ pəs) *n.* a warm-blooded marine mammal that is related to the dolphin.

por-tion (pôr′ shən) *n.* **1.** a part of a whole: *We spent a portion of the day at the park.* **2.** a part or share of a whole belonging to a person or a group. **3.** a helping of food served to one person. *-v.* to divide into parts or shares.

por-tray (pôr trā′) *v.* **1.** to draw or paint a picture of: *The artist portrayed the beautiful mountains in a painting.* **2.** to give a picture of in words; describe.

1. Which word can be used as either a noun

    or a verb? _____

2. Which entry word has the most example

    sentences? _____

3. What part of speech is <u>porpoise</u>?

    _____

n.	noun
pron.	pronoun
v.	verb
adj.	adjective
adv.	adverb
prep.	preposition

4. How many definitions are given for the word <u>porpoise</u>? _____

    for <u>portion</u>? _____   for <u>portray</u>? _____

5. Write the most commonly used definition of <u>popular</u>. _____

    _____

6. Use the first definition of <u>popular</u> in a sentence. _____

    _____

7. Write a sentence in which you use <u>portion</u> as a verb. _____

    _____

8. Use the second definition of <u>portray</u> in a sentence. _____

    _____

Dictionary: Etymologies

- Many dictionary entries include an **etymology** which is the origin and development of a word.
- An etymology is usually enclosed in brackets [ ] after the definition of the entry word. The symbol < stands for the phrase "is derived from" or "comes from."

    EXAMPLE: **razor** [Middle English *rasor* < Old French *raser,* to scrape.]
    The word razor came into English from the Middle English word rasor, which came from the Old French word raser, which meant "to scrape."

- **Use the dictionary entries below to answer the questions.**

nov-el (nov´əl) *n.* a long piece of prose fiction with a detailed plot. *-adj.* new, strange, unusual. [Old French *novelle,* unique, from Latin *novella,* new things.]

pueb-lo (pweb´lō) *n* **1.** a Native American dwelling made of adobe and stone which houses many people. **2. Pueblo.** a member of a Native American tribe that lives in pueblos. [Spanish *pueblo,* people or village, from Latin *populus,* people.]

punk (pungk) *n.* **1.** a dry, light, brownish substance that burns very slowly, often used to light fireworks. **2.** dry, decayed wood, used in its dry state as tinder. [Probably from Algonquin *punk,* live ashes.]

reef (rēf) *n.* part of a sail that can be rolled or folded up to reduce the amount of the sail exposed to the wind. *-v.* to roll or fold up a part of a sail. [Old Norse *rifridge.*]

1. Which word probably came from the Algonquin language? _____

2. Which languages are in the history of the word novel?

   _____

3. Which word originally meant "live ashes"? _____

4. Which word comes from the word populus? _____

5. Which words have more than one language in their history? _____

   _____

6. What is the meaning of the Latin word novella? _____

7. Which word is spelled the same in English as it is in Spanish?

   _____

8. From what language did the Old French word novelle come?

   _____

9. Which words came into English from only one earlier language? _____

   _____

10. Which word comes from a word that meant "people"? _____

11. Which word comes from the word rifridge? _____

> - A **title page** tells the name of a book and its author.
> - A **copyright page** tells who published the book, where it was published, and when it was published.
> - A **table of contents** lists the chapter or unit titles and the page numbers on which they begin. It is at the front of a book.
> - An **index** gives a detailed list of the topics in a book and the page numbers on which each topic is found. It is in the back of a book.

A. Use your *Language Exercises* book to answer the questions.

1. What is the title? _____

2. What company published this book? _____

3. On what page does Unit 6 start? _____

4. Where is the index located? _____

5. What is the copyright date? _____

6. What pages contain lessons on outlining? _____

7. On what page does Unit 4 start? _____

8. On what pages are the lessons on irregular verbs found?

   _____

9. What lesson is on page 38? _____

10. List the pages that deal with singular and plural nouns. _____

    _____

11. On what page is the lesson on gerunds found? _____

12. On what page is the lesson on idioms found? _____

13. On what page does Unit 2 start? _____

B. Answer the questions below.

1. Where would you look to find the name of a a book's author?

   _____

2. Where would you look if you wanted to know how many chapters were in a book?

   _____

3. Where would you find the year in which a book was published?

   _____

4. Where would you find out the page number on which a particular topic is found?

   _____

- A **chart** lists information in columns, which you read down, and rows, which you read across. The information can be either words or numbers.
- A **graph** shows how a quantity or quantities change over time. It often shows how two or more things change in relation to one another. The information can be shown by lines, dots, bars, pictures, or in a circle.

A. Use the chart and the graph to answer the questions below.

Yard Work Chart

Month	Hours Spent by Carlos	Hours Spent by Karen
April	21	23
May	26	26
June	29	26
July	30	29
August	24	25

Yard Work Graph

Graph Key
Karen _____
Carlos _ _ _ _ _ _ _

1. Who spent more hours doing yard work in April? _____

   in July? _____

2. During which two months did Karen spend the same amount of time on her yard work?

   _____

3. During what month did Karen and Carlos spend the same amount of time on

   their yard work? _____

4. Is it quicker to determine from the chart or from the graph the exact number of hours

   either person spent each month? _____

5. Is it quicker to determine from the chart or from the graph how Carlos's and Karen's

   yard work schedules changed over the months? _____

- A **road map** is another valuable type of visual aid. Maps like the one shown below are helpful when you are unfamiliar with a certain area. To use any map, you should refer to its **legend, compass rose,** and **scale.**
- The legend tells what each symbol on the map represents.
- The compass rose is made up of arrows that point north, south, east, and west.
- The scale allows you to determine how far it is from one location to another. To use the scale, mark the distance between any two locations along the edge of a sheet of paper. Then place the sheet of paper alongside the scale of distance, lining up one of the marks with zero. This will allow you to read the distance between the two locations.

B. Use the map to answer the questions below.

Green Point Area

1. Is the business district east or west of the golf course? _____

2. On what road do you find the fairgrounds? _____

3. How many miles is it from Route 69 to Lake Wigwam? _____

4. What kind of highway is 69? _____

5. Is the courthouse within the business district? _____

6. Does Elm Street run north/south or east/west? _____

7. How many exit ramps are there on Route 69 between Cherry Lane and Route 70? _____

8. How many miles will you travel if you drive from Buckingham Fountain

   to Fort Tucker National Monument? _____

■ Books are arranged on library shelves according to **call numbers.** Each book is assigned a number from 000 to 999, according to its subject matter. The following are the main subject groups for call numbers:

000–099 Reference	500–599 Science and Mathematics
100–199 Philosophy	600–699 Technology
200–299 Religion	700–799 The Arts
300–399 Social Sciences	800–899 Literature
400–499 Languages	900–999 History and Geography

A. Write the call number group in which you would find each book.

1. *Australia: The Island Continent* _____

2. *Technology in a New Age* _____

3. *French: A Romance Language* _____

4. *Solving Word Problems in Mathematics* _____

5. *Ancient Philosophy* _____

6. *2006 World Almanac and Book of Facts* _____

7. *Artists of the 1920's* _____

8. *Funny Poems for a Rainy Day* _____

9. *Science Experiments for Teen-agers* _____

10. *People in Society* _____

11. *Russian Folktales* _____

12. *Religions Around the World* _____

13. *World War I: The Complete Story* _____

14. *Encyclopaedia Britannica* _____

15. *The Social Characteristics of Pack Animals* _____

B. Write the titles of three of your favorite books. Write the call number range beside each title.

1. _____

2. _____

3. _____

- The **card catalog** contains information cards on every book in the library. Some libraries are now computerized and have no card catalogs, but the information in the computer is filed in the same manner as the information in the card catalog.
- Each book has three cards in the catalog. They are filed separately according to:
  1. the author's last name
  2. the subject of the book
  3. the title of the book

A. Use the sample catalog card to answer the questions below.

Author Card

Call number — | 331.20 Le | Leventhal, Robert — Author

Title — A Great Place to Visit

Place published — —New York: | Phantom House Inc. — Publisher

Date published — © 1993

Number of pages — 312 p.

1. Who is the author? _____

2. Are there any pictures or drawings in the book? _____

3. What is the book's call number? _____

4. When was the book published? _____

5. List one subject under which the subject card for this book might be filed. _____

6. Write what the heading would be for this book's title card. _____

B. Write author, title, **or** subject **to tell which card you would look for to locate the book or books.**

1. books about sports in Russia _____

2. a novel by Mark Twain _____

3. *The Invisible Man* _____

4. books about Amelia Earhart _____

5. a book of poems by Emily Dickinson _____

6. *It's a Dog's Life* _____

Lesson
80

Using an Encyclopedia

- An **encyclopedia** is a reference book that contains articles on many different topics. The articles are arranged alphabetically in volumes. Each volume is marked to indicate which articles are inside.
- **Guide words** are used to show the first topic on each page.
- At the end of most articles there is a listing of **cross-references** that suggests related topics for the reader to investigate.
- Most encyclopedias also have an index of subject titles.

A. Find the entry for <u>Louisa May Alcott</u> in an encyclopedia. Then answer the following questions.

1. What encyclopedia did you use? _____

2. When did Louisa May Alcott live? _____

3. Where was she born? _____

4. What is the name of one of her books? _____

5. What did she do as a volunteer during the American Civil War? _____

B. Find the entry for <u>Medic Alert</u> in an encyclopedia. Then answer the questions.

1. What encyclopedia did you use? _____

2. The Medic Alert emblem can be worn as a _____.

3. What organization provides the Medic Alert emblems? _____

4. What kind of information does the emblem give about the person wearing it?

_____

5. Whose telephone number appears on the emblem? _____

C. Find the entry in an encyclopedia for a person in whom you are interested. Then answer the following questions.

1. Who is your subject? _____

2. What encyclopedia did you use? _____

3. When did the person live? _____

4. What is it about the person that makes him or her famous? _____

_____

5. What cross-references are listed? _____

_____

- Most encyclopedias have an **index** of subject titles, listed in alphabetical order.
- The index shows the volume and the page number where an article is found.
- Some encyclopedias contain articles on many different topics. Some encyclopedias contain many different articles relating to a broad general topic.

■ **Use the sample encyclopedia index entry to answer the questions.**

Index
Alligator, 1–6; 11–389; *see* Crocodile; Reptile
Bear, 1–35
    Black, 1–37
    Brown, 1–36
    Grizzly, 1–37
    Polar, 1–39
Cougar, 2–53; *see* Bobcat; Mountain Lion
Crocodile, 2–79; 11–389 *see* Alligator; Reptile
Dingo, 3–94

1. In what volume would you find an article on grizzly bears? _____

2. On what pages would you find information on crocodiles? _____

3. Are all articles on bears found in the same volume? _____

4. On page 6 you would find an article about what animal? _____

5. What are the cross-references for **Alligator**? _____

6. Do the words in bold show the name of the volume or the name of the animal? _____

7. Which animals have articles in two volumes? _____

8. In which volume would you expect to find information on reptiles? _____

9. Information on what animal is found in Volume 3? _____

10. If you looked under **Bobcat**, what might you expect to find as cross-references? _____

11. Information on what animal is found on page 79 in the encyclopedia? _____

12. Which of the following would be the most likely title of this encyclopedia? _____

    a. Encyclopedia of Reptiles   **b.** Encyclopedia of Mammals   **c.** Encyclopedia of Wild Animals

Using a Thesaurus

> ■ A **thesaurus** is a reference book that writers use to find the exact
> words they need. Like a dictionary, a thesaurus lists its entry words
> alphabetically. Each entry word has a list of **synonyms,** or words that
> can be used in its place. Some thesauruses also list **antonyms** for the
> entry word.
>   EXAMPLE: You have just written the following sentence:
>   The children **laughed** as the tiny puppy licked their faces.
>   With the help of a thesaurus, you could improve the sentence
>   by replacing laughed with its more precise synonym giggled.
>   The children **giggled** as the tiny puppy licked their faces.

A. Use the thesaurus sample below to answer the questions.

> **move** *v. syn.* turn, budge, shift, retrieve, carry, transport,
> retreat, crawl, arouse, progress. *ant.* stay, stop, stabilize

1. Which is the entry word? _____

2. What are its synonyms? _____

   _____

3. Which word would you use in place of excite? _____

4. Which word would you use in place of rotate? _____

5. What are the antonyms of move? _____

6. Which antonym would you use in place of remain? _____

B. Use the synonyms of move to complete the sentences.

1. Sharon asked me if I would _____ the groceries in from the car.

2. Spot was able to _____ the golf ball from the lake.

3. Ryan's job is to _____ fruit from Michigan to other parts of the country.

4. The surfer had to _____ his weight from one leg to the other to
   keep his balance.

5. The instructor asked the students to _____ around in their chairs so they
   could see the map.

6. A baby has to _____ in order to get around.

7. We hope to _____ steadily up the mountain by climbing from ledge to ledge.

8. Robert wouldn't _____ from his favorite spot under the kitchen table.

■ The **Readers' Guide to Periodical Literature** lists by author and by subject all the articles that appear in nearly two hundred magazines. Use the *Readers' Guide* when you need
- recent articles on a particular subject,
- several articles written over a period of time about the same subject,
- many articles written by the same author.

■ **Use the *Readers' Guide* samples to answer the questions below.**

Subject Entry

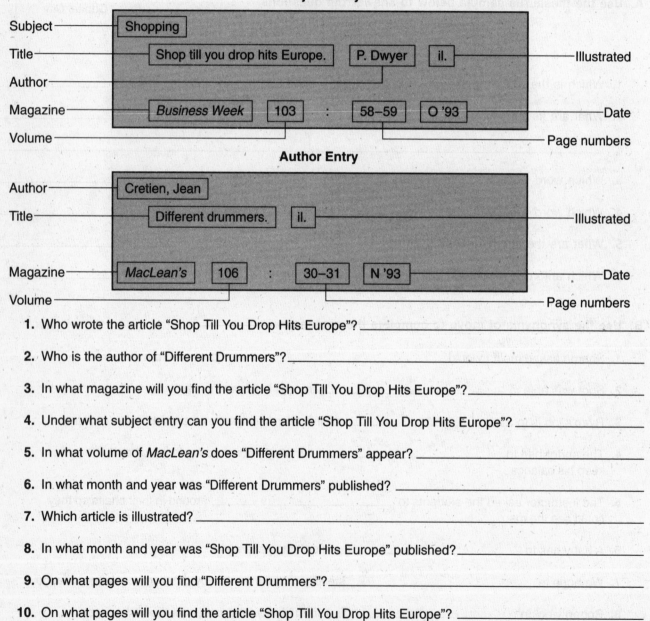

Subject — Shopping

Title — Shop till you drop hits Europe.   P. Dwyer   il. — Illustrated
Author

Magazine — *Business Week*   103   :   58–59   O '93 — Date
Volume — Page numbers

Author Entry

Author — Cretien, Jean

Title — Different drummers.   il. — Illustrated

Magazine — *MacLean's*   106   :   30–31   N '93 — Date
Volume — Page numbers

1. Who wrote the article "Shop Till You Drop Hits Europe"? _____

2. Who is the author of "Different Drummers"? _____

3. In what magazine will you find the article "Shop Till You Drop Hits Europe"? _____

4. Under what subject entry can you find the article "Shop Till You Drop Hits Europe"? _____

5. In what volume of *MacLean's* does "Different Drummers" appear? _____

6. In what month and year was "Different Drummers" published? _____

7. Which article is illustrated? _____

8. In what month and year was "Shop Till You Drop Hits Europe" published? _____

9. On what pages will you find "Different Drummers"? _____

10. On what pages will you find the article "Shop Till You Drop Hits Europe"? _____

Using an Atlas

> ■ An **atlas** is a reference book that uses maps to organize pertinent facts
> about states, provinces, countries, continents, and bodies of water.
> Additional maps show information on topography; resources, industry, and
> agriculture; vegetation; population; and climate.

A. Use the sample atlas entry to answer the questions below.

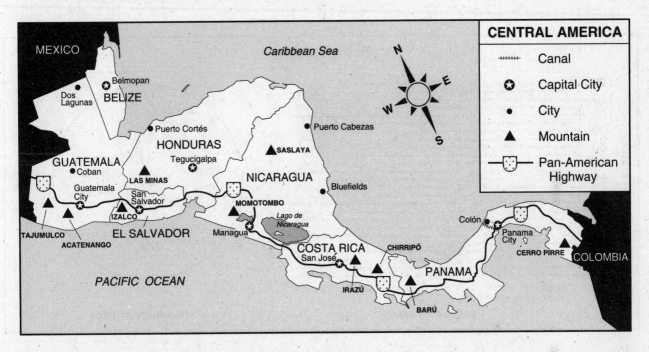

1. What part of the world is shown on this map? _____

2. How many countries make up Central America? _____

3. Which mountain is farthest west? _____

4. What major highway is shown on the map?_____

5. Which country has no mountains?_____

6. What is the capital of Nicaragua? _____

B. Answer the questions.

1. What kind of map would you use to find out where most mining occurs in a country?_____

2. Would a topographical map show you where the most people live or where the most mountains are? _____

   _____

3. What kind of map would you use to decide what clothes to pack for a July trip to Japan? _____

- An **almanac** is a reference book that presents useful information on a wide variety of topics. Much of this information is in the form of tables, charts, graphs, and time lines.

- **Use the sample almanac page to answer the questions.**

1. Which trip accounts for the most miles traveled? _____

2. What reason do most people give for taking trips? _____

3. Which three purposes together account for 60% of all trips? _____

4. Which graph shows how often people travel for a specific purpose? _____

5. Which trips are the shortest? _____

6. Do people travel farther for work or for social reasons? _____

7. Out of 100 trips, how many are made for shopping/business reasons? _____

8. What is the length of the trip least often taken? _____

9. What is the length of the trip most often taken? _____

10. Do people travel more often for school/church or for social reasons? _____

- Use a **dictionary** to find definitions of words, pronunciations of words, word usage suggestions, and etymologies, or word histories.
- Use an **encyclopedia** to find articles about many different people and things. Also use an encyclopedia to find references to related subjects.
- Use a **thesaurus** to find synonyms and antonyms.
- Use the ***Readers' Guide to Periodical Literature*** to find magazine articles on specific subjects or by particular authors.
- Use an **atlas** to find maps and other information about geographical locations.
- Use an **almanac** to find information such as population numbers, annual rainfall, election statistics, and other specific information over a period of one year.

■ Write **dictionary, encyclopedia, thesaurus,** *Readers' Guide,* **atlas,** or **almanac** to show where you would find the following information. Some information might be found in more than one source.

_____ 1. the depth of the Indian Ocean

_____ 2. the definition of the word <u>animosity</u>

_____ 3. an article on parachuting

_____ 4. the usages of the word <u>speckle</u>

_____ 5. a synonym for the word <u>build</u>

_____ 6. an article on the latest development in cancer research

_____ 7. the pronunciation of the word <u>pneumonia</u>

_____ 8. the largest lake in Louisiana

_____ 9. facts about the life of Abraham Lincoln

_____ 10. a synonym for the word <u>begin</u>

_____ 11. information about John F. Kennedy's presidency

_____ 12. the origin of the word <u>immortal</u>

_____ 13. recent articles on home fire prevention

_____ 14. the history of the French Revolution

_____ 15. the average January temperature in Santa Fe, New Mexico

_____ 16. the states through which the Mississippi River runs

_____ 17. an antonym for the word <u>answer</u>

Using Reference Sources

■ Use reference sources—dictionaries, encyclopedias, the *Readers' Guide to Periodical Literature,* thesauruses, atlases, and almanacs—to find information about people, places, or things with which you are not familiar. You can also use these sources to learn more about subjects that interest you.

A. Follow the directions below.

1. Find the entry for your state in one of the reference sources. Write the exact title

   of the reference source. _____

2. Write a brief summary of the information you found about your state.

   _____

   _____

   _____

   _____

   _____

   _____

B. Follow the directions, and answer the questions.

1. Choose a famous person you would like to know more about.

   Person's name: _____

2. List two reference sources you can use to find information about this person.

   1. _____ 2. _____

3. Use one of the sources you listed above to find out when the person was born.

   Write the date of birth. _____

4. Use the appropriate reference source to find the title of the most recent article written about the person. Write the title of the article.

   _____

5. Use either reference source you listed in number two. Find the entry for the person you are researching. Write a short summary of the information you found.

   _____

   _____

   _____

C. Follow the directions, and answer the questions.

1. Choose a country you would like to learn more about.

   Name of country: _____

2. List four reference sources you can use to find information about this country.

   1. _____   3. _____

   2. _____   4. _____

3. Use one reference source to find the title of the most recent article
   written about the country. Write the title of the article.

   _____

4. Use one reference source to find out the capital of the country. Write the name

   of the capital. _____

5. Use another reference source to find out on what continent the country is located.

   Write the name of the continent. _____

6. Find the entry for the country in any one of the reference sources you
   listed in number two. Write the exact title of the reference source.

   _____

7. Write a short summary of the information you found. Do not include
   information given in number 3, 4, or 5.

   _____

   _____

   _____

   _____

   _____

8. Find the entry for the country in one other reference source. Write

   the exact title of the reference source. _____

9. What new information did you learn about the country?

   _____

   _____

   _____

A. Use the dictionary samples to answer the questions below.

De-cem-ber (di sem' bər) *n.* the twelfth month of the year. It has thirty-one days. [Latin *December,* which was the tenth month in the early Roman calendar, from *decem,* ten.]
den-im (den' im) *n.* **1.** a heavy, coarse cotton cloth. **2. denims** clothing made of denim. [Short for French *(serge) de Nîmes,* a French town where the fabric was originally made.]
de-sert (dez' ərt) *n.* a hot, dry area with few plants or animals. *-adj.* **1.** dry and barren; found in a desert: *a*

desert cactus. **2.** not inhabited: *a desert island.* [Old French *desert;* going back to Latin *desertum,* something abandoned, forsaken.]
di-et (dī' ət) *n.* **1.** a person's or animal's usual food and drink: *A lion's diet includes meat and vegetables.* **2.** a prescribed selection of food and drink: *I hope to lose ten pounds on my diet.* *-v.* to eat following certain rules: *I will diet to lose weight.* [Old French *diete;* going back to Greek *diaita,* way of life.]

1. How many syllables does <u>diet</u> have? _____ desert? _____ December? _____

2. What word was named after a French town? _____

3. What part of speech is <u>December</u>? _____ denim? _____

4. From what languages did the word <u>diet</u> come? _____

5. Write the correct word for each respelling.

   a. (dez' ərt) _____ **b.** (di sem' bər) _____

6. Write one sentence using the second definition of <u>desert</u>. _____

   _____

7. What word originally meant "way of life"? _____

8. Through what other languages did the word <u>desert</u> come into English? _____

9. Which words can be used as more than one part of speech? _____

10. Which word comes from a word meaning "ten"? _____

B. Write <u>title page</u>, <u>copyright page</u>, <u>table of contents</u>, or <u>index</u> to tell where to find this information in a book.

_____ 1. the chapter titles

_____ 2. the page number on which a particular topic can be found

_____ 3. the name of the publisher

_____ 4. the author's name

_____ 5. the year the book was published

_____ 6. how many chapters are in the book

_____ 7. the page number on which a certain chapter begins

_____ 8. where the book was published

C. Use the graph and the chart to answer the questions below.

Pounds of Nuts Collected

Name	Percent of Total		
	Week 1	Week 2	Week 3
Sharon	10	23	10
Alberto	27	25	28
Linn	45	12	33
Ellis	18	40	29

Pounds of Nuts Collected

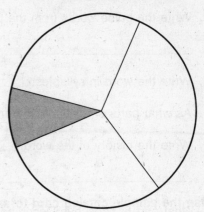

1. Which person collected the greatest percentage of nuts in Week 2? _____

2. Which person collected the total highest percentage of nuts? _____

3. Which person's total percentage is shown by the shaded portion of the graph? _____

D. Write dictionary, encyclopedia, card catalog, thesaurus, atlas, almanac, or *Readers' Guide* to show where you would find the following information.

_____ 1. a chart of data on the 2006 Winter Olympics

_____ 2. whether a book has illustrations

_____ 3. an article about earthworms

_____ 4. an antonym for the word charitable

_____ 5. a recent magazine article on computers

_____ 6. a map of the vegetation of Missouri

_____ 7. the author of a book

_____ 8. the origin of the word buffalo

_____ 9. cross-references for a topic

_____ 10. the most mountainous area of Argentina

A. Find the word <u>condition</u> in a dictionary. Then follow the directions, and answer the questions.

1. Write the guide words from the page on which you found the entry for <u>condition</u>.

_____

2. Write the word in syllables. _____

3. As what parts of speech can <u>condition</u> be used? _____

4. Write the history of the word. _____

_____

B. Use the sample catalog card to answer the questions.

> 808.51
> Eh
>   **Ehrlich, Henry**
>   Writing effective speeches.   New York,
> Paragon House
> [1992] 214 p.

1. What type of catalog card is this? _____

2. What is the title of the book? _____

3. Who is the author of the book? _____

4. Is the book illustrated? _____

C. Find the entry for <u>apricot</u> in an encyclopedia. Then answer the questions.

1. Name three ways in which apricots are used as food. _____

2. Are the pits of apricots ever edible? _____

3. How tall can the apricot tree grow? _____

D. Use the *Readers' Guide* entry to answer the questions.

> **KERNS, LESLIE ANN**
>   The trouble with money. *Time* 68: 32–34 Je '88

1. Who wrote the article? _____

2. What is the title of the article? _____

3. In what magazine does the article appear? _____

4. Is the article illustrated? _____

E. Use the information in the chart to complete the graph. Then answer the questions below.

Average Number of Hours Spent on Sports by College Students (Per Month)

Chart

Month	Hours Spent by Students in Florida	Hours Spent by Students in Minnesota
January	40	15
March	30	25
May	25	40
July	15	35
September	20	30
November	30	15

Graph

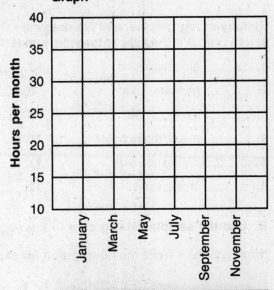

Graph Key
Students in Florida _____
Students in Minnesota _ _ _ _ _ _

1. In November, what is the average number of hours students in Florida spend

   participating in sports? _____   students in Minnesota? _____

2. During which two months do students in Florida spend the same average amount

   of time on sports? _____

3. During which month are students in Minnesota the most active in sports?

   _____   students in Florida? _____

4. Is there a month during which the average amount of time spent on sports is the same

   for students in Minnesota and students in Florida? _____

F. Find a resource map of Mexico in an atlas. Then answer the questions.

1. On which coast is most of the food processing done? _____

2. What mineral is mined in the Yucatan Peninsula? _____

3. What is Mexico's major crop? _____

4. What resource is found on all the coastlines of Mexico? _____

Synonyms, Antonyms, and Homonyms ▪ On the line before each pair of words, write S if they are synonyms, A if they are antonyms, and H if they are homonyms.

1. _____ aloud, allowed

2. _____ genuine, fake

3. _____ clever, smart

4. _____ threw, through

5. _____ brave, cowardly

6. _____ crave, want

7. _____ greedy, generous

8. _____ their, there

9. _____ calm, peaceful

10. _____ beech, beach

11. _____ quiet, silent

12. _____ alter, altar

13. _____ unattractive, ugly

14. _____ bloom, flower

15. _____ heard, herd

16. _____ bent, crooked

17. _____ off, on

18. _____ by, buy

Homographs ▪ Write the homograph for each pair of meanings below.

1. **a.** get down from   **b.** on fire   _____

2. **a.** from a higher to a lower place   **b.** soft feathers   _____

3. **a.** take up a weapon   **b.** part of the body   _____

4. **a.** to walk softly   **b.** a pillow   _____

5. **a.** loud noise   **b.** mesh bat used in certain sports   _____

6. **a.** to rip or pull apart   **b.** salty liquid from the eye   _____

7. **a.** belonging to me   **b.** to dig for metals or minerals   _____

8. **a.** one devoted to another   **b.** a device to stir air   _____

Prefixes, Suffixes, and Compound Words ▪ Write P if the underlined word has a prefix, write S if it has a suffix, and write C if it is a compound word.

1. _____ _____ It is time to <u>remove</u> the plates from the <u>dishwasher</u>.

2. _____ _____ Dr. Arnold is a <u>famous</u> doctor and research <u>scientist</u>.

3. _____ _____ The scouts built a <u>campfire</u> and planned to <u>rearrange</u> their tents.

4. _____ _____ They will be at a <u>disadvantage</u> if they <u>mismanage</u> the budget.

5. _____ _____ <u>Unpleasant</u> weather is predicted for the <u>weekend</u>.

6. _____ _____ Please be <u>careful</u> when you toss the <u>newspaper</u> onto the porch.

7. _____ _____ It seemed <u>impossible</u> that the jacket was <u>repairable</u>.

8. _____ _____ The <u>dusty</u> attic made my <u>grandmother</u> sneeze.

9. _____ _____ Iris and Bruce are <u>coauthors</u> of the <u>newsletter</u>.

10. _____ _____ Her <u>impish</u> grin made her seem more <u>childlike</u> than she truly was.

Contractions ▪ Write the contraction for each pair of words.

1. I have _____
2. we will _____
3. they are _____
4. could not _____
5. you have _____
6. do not _____

7. he had _____
8. I am _____
9. that is _____
10. did not _____
11. will not _____
12. there is _____

13. they will _____
14. we had _____
15. does not _____
16. it is _____
17. would not _____
18. I will _____

Connotation, Denotation, Idioms ▪ For each underlined word or words, write (–) for a negative connotation, (+) for a positive connotation, or (N) for a neutral connotation. Write I if the words make an idiom.

1. _____ The sleek horse galloped.
2. _____ She ran like the wind.
3. _____ A skinny scarecrow watched.
4. _____ An old jalopy drove by us.
5. _____ A vicious dog growled.
6. _____ I plan to drop her a line.
7. _____ The brilliant sun shone.
8. _____ It lit up the sky.

9. _____ A colorful kite flew overhead.
10. _____ An airplane carried many people.
11. _____ We stood by shooting the breeze.
12. _____ It was a relaxing afternoon.
13. _____ Two children giggled.
14. _____ Everyone gulped their lemonade.
15. _____ No one felt down in the dumps.
16. _____ Everyone got in the car and left.

Idioms ▪ For the underlined idiom in each sentence below, write the usual meaning of the words that make up the idiom.

1. You need to keep your chin up. _____

2. It really gets my goat when people litter. _____

3. I burned the midnight oil studying for that test. _____

4. She really dropped the ball on that project. _____

5. I resolved to turn over a new leaf. _____

6. I ran across some old photos in the attic. _____

7. I work two jobs to make ends meet. _____

8. I threw in the towel after trying for two hours to fix the car. _____

9. We had to eat crow when their team won the game. _____

10. Joanne spilled the beans about the surprise party. _____

Types of Sentences ▪ Before each sentence, write D for declarative, IN for interrogative, IM for imperative, and E for exclamatory. Punctuate each sentence correctly.

1. _____ This dinner is delicious___

2. _____ Please pass the pepper___

3. _____ Where are the forks___

4. _____ I'm starving___

5. _____ What's in that bowl___

6. _____ Does anyone want more___

7. _____ Ouch, I burned my tongue___

8. _____ I'd like another roll___

9. _____ Eat more slowly___

10. _____ Who wants to clear the table___

Parts of a Sentence ▪ Underline the word or words in each sentence that are identified in parentheses.

1. (compound predicate)   Ellen typed and proofread her report.

2. (indirect object)   Matt, lend me your black pen.

3. (simple subject)   The report is excellent.

4. (direct object)   The instructor gave the report an "A."

5. (subordinate clause)   The first draft that Ellen wrote was 12 pages long.

6. (complete predicate)   She read her notes six times.

7. (complete subject)   Everyone in the class chose a different subject.

8. (simple predicate)   All the reports were completed in two weeks.

9. (independent clause)   The reports had to be in on time, or they would lose a grade.

10. (adverb clause)   I finished before the due date.

Parts of a Sentence ▪ Underline each subordinate clause. Then write adjective or adverb on the line.

_____ 1. The lawyer who defended the criminal was just doing her job.

_____ 2. The concert was over before we knew it.

_____ 3. It was the first time that Edward had been to Niagara Falls.

_____ 4. Although it was still early, Pamela left to go home.

_____ 5. Canada is a beautiful country that people like to visit.

_____ 6. When Rebecca heard that, she became very angry.

_____ 7. The horse kicked because it had never been saddled before.

_____ 8. Safety has become more important since the crime rate began to rise.

_____ 9. The people whose last names begin with "M" can enter now.

_____ 10. After the way Joe acted, I don't want to see him again.

Complex Sentences ▪ To each group of words below, add a subordinate clause or an independent clause to create a complex sentence.

1. Paul forgot the directions _____

2. After it was dark _____

3. This wasn't planned _____

4. When we took a couple of wrong turns _____

5. Before crossing the bridge _____

6. While looking for a map _____

7. When he asked for directions _____

8. No one had heard of the street _____

9. Three hours later _____

10. Before the trip home _____

Compound Sentences ▪ Create compound sentences by adding an independent clause to each group of words.

1. Walter bought a new hunting dog _____

2. She called to change her tickets _____

3. It was too late for Tom _____

4. We decided to stay at home _____

5. Leaders from several countries came _____

6. You can leave it there _____

7. It's possible that I am wrong _____

8. The wind picked up _____

Run-on Sentences ▪ Correct each run-on sentence by writing it as two sentences or as a compound sentence.

1. It was the middle of the night, the smoke alarm went off we woke up frightened.

_____

2. The reason we called you here is clear, we need to make some decisions today.

_____

Expanding Sentences ▪ Expand the sentence by adding details to answer the questions What kind? and How many? Write the expanded sentence on the line.

The butterflies migrated.

_____

Grammar and Usage ▪ Fill in the blanks by following the directions in parentheses.

The art of growing and _____ miniature trees is called Bonsai. The
(gerund)

Japanese word <u>bonsai</u> means "tray-planted." The Chinese first _____
(transitive verb)

bonsai over 1,000 years ago. Growing bonsai became _____ popular in
(adverb)

Japan in the 1800s. It _____ been a hobby _____
(helping verb)   (preposition)

the United States since the early 1900s and is still _____ in popularity.
(present participle)

Bonsai trees are normal trees _____ are made _____
(relative pronoun)   (preposition)

miniatures. They can be made from _____ types of trees, including
(adjective)

evergreens, pines, flowering, and fruit trees. It takes much skill, time, and _____
(abstract noun)

to make the bonsai tree look like a miniature replica of a tree in nature. Gardeners must

practice for years to _____ how to make bonsai. The bonsai
(teach or learn)

_____ are pruned and wired _____
(plural of branch)   (infinitive)

desired shapes. The dwarfed roots are kept in small containers and also pruned to stunt

_____ growth.
(possessive pronoun)

A bonsai tree ranges _____ height from two inches to two or three
(preposition)

feet. Would you _____ that a smaller tree takes much longer
(present perfect tense of <u>guess</u>)

(sometimes ten years) to achieve _____ ideal shape and size? It
(its or it's)

can grow inside _____ outside. In Japan, the healthiest and
(conjunction)

_____ bonsai are kept outside _____ are
(superlative adjective)   (conjunction)

only brought inside for viewing. _____ live for 100 years or more. In
(indefinite pronoun)

Japan, many _____ families pass them down _____
(proper adjective)   (preposition)

the next generation as a _____ heirloom.
(adjective)

Nouns ▪ Draw a line under each noun in the sentences below. Then write C or P above it to show whether it is a common or proper noun. On the line, identify each common noun as concrete, abstract, or collective.

_____ 1. Niagara Falls is on the border between the United States and Canada.

_____ 2. The citizens voted overwhelmingly for Judge Harriman.

_____ 3. Daniel showed his courage by diving into Lake Michigan.

Singular and Plural Nouns ▪ Write the plural for each singular noun.

1. volcano _____

2. painting _____

3. bench _____

4. deer _____

5. woman _____

6. mother-in-law _____

Possessive Nouns ▪ Write the possessive form of each noun below.

1. authors_____

2. men _____

3. highway_____

4. sky _____

5. envelope_____

6. Donna _____

Verbs ▪ Fill in the blank with the correct form of the verb in parentheses.

1. (show)   He has _____ his parents a great deal of respect.

2. (take)   I _____ this same route many times before.

3. (do)   Have you _____ your chores yet?

4. (speak)   She _____ more loudly than was necessary.

Pronouns ▪ Write subject, object, possessive, demonstrative, or indefinite to label each underlined pronoun.

_____ 1. Phillip gave his sister a new bicycle.

_____ 2. Do you think these are the right size?

_____ 3. They went deep-sea fishing on their vacation.

Adjectives and Adverbs ▪ Underline the correct word.

1. Roberto plays most sports very (good, well).

2. Run (quickly, quick) to the other side of the street.

3. She is the (happier, happiest) person I know.

Prepositions and Prepositional Phrases ▪ Underline each prepositional phrase. Then circle each preposition.

1. Her friend lives in the red house on the left side of the street.

2. People ran to the windows to watch the wrecking ball crash into the building.

Capitalization and End Punctuation ▪ Circle each letter that should be capitalized. Write the capital letter above it. Add the correct end punctuation to each sentence.

1. our neighborhood holds a block party every june____

2. will the organizers be mrs. hernandez and dr. altman____

3. a local restaurant, charlie's place, is donating pizzas and italian sandwiches____

4. my street will be closed off on saturday and sunday from clark st. to prairie lane____

5. mr. johnson of the store bikes for you is judging the bicycle decorating contest____

6. will the country kitchen at oakland ave. donate 100 pies for the pie-eating contest____

7. last year's champion, mark gable of rosemont, says, "i'm ready for all

   the blueberry pies you can give me____"

8. dancers and singers from the phillips school will perform scenes from

   robert louis stevenson's *treasure island*____

9. the road race begins at the corner of maple and crane streets at 8:00 A.M. on saturday____

10. there are runners entered from carlyle, rosemont, meadow grove, and newton____

Using Other Punctuation ▪ Add commas, quotation marks, and apostrophes where needed in the sentences below.

1. Why are you telling me all this now asked Cynthia.
2. You can use books encyclopedias and atlases when doing research.
3. Ive spent the last two hours waiting said Mary.
4. Scott said Youll be much happier when you get settled.
5. Lloyd Jane and Debra are all going in the same car.
6. Wont you please help me with this asked Joe.
7. Shes the one said Ellen who brought that wonderful dessert.
8. Nissans Hondas and Toyotas are Japanese automobiles.
9. My fruit salad recipe she said calls for oranges apples bananas and raisins.
10. Karen mowed the yard weeded the garden and watered the flowers.
11. Saras car was in the shop for two weeks.
12. Janet Rosa and Alicia went to Dianes dinner party.

Punctuation and Capitalization ▪ Circle each letter that should be capitalized. Add commas, quotation marks, apostrophes, periods, hyphens, and colons where needed.

1230 e. clark st.
san diego, ca 94024

mr. charles martinelli
3340 w. belden street
san diego, ca 94022

Dear mr. martinelli

 on june 10 and 11, our neighborhood will be holding its fifth-anniversary summer block party____ it is a day-long event with contests performances great food and sidewalk sales____ in past years, local restaurants and businesses have donated food and prizes____ we hope your restaurant charlies place will join in and help make our block party a success____ i remember you once saying id love to pitch in next time____ please call us at 555 1270 and let us know if youll want to contribute this year____ we look forward to hearing from you soon____

Sincerely,
angela hernandez

Using Other Punctuation ▪ Add colons, semicolons, hyphens, dashes, and underlining where needed in the sentences below.

1. You mean that you said and I'm quoting you now that he was "too big for his britches"?
2. I read Lonesome Dove three times it was such a wonderful book.
3. I addressed my greeting "Dear Madam or Sir " since I didn't know whether the owner was a man or a woman.
4. The festival Saturday runs from 1000 A.M. to 500 P.M.
5. Tony bought a blue green convertible when he got his new job.
6. My sister in law writes children's stories they are also fun for adults to read.
7. My favorite show is on every Tuesday at 800 it's the best show on television.
8. The local play had parts for seventy eight people men, women, and children were invited to audition.
9. I use the money from my part time job to pay for these hobbies photography, dancing, and horseback riding.
10. Connie has seen her favorite movie, Gone With the Wind, twenty two times.

Expanding Sentences ▪ **Expand the meaning of each sentence base below by adding adjectives, adverbs, and/or prepositional phrases.**

1. (Airplanes flew.) _____

2. (Dogs barked.) _____

3. (Painter brushed.) _____

Topic Sentences ▪ **Write a topic sentence for the paragraph below.**

Many parents encourage their children to take music lessons. Some people learn to play music immediately. Others take longer to master the skill. Practicing improves your skills and helps you learn discipline. Most adults who play instruments, whether professionally or just for fun, are thankful that they started playing as children.

Topic Sentence: _____

Supporting Details ▪ **Write an X before the sentences that support the topic sentence.**

Topic Sentence: House plants are a good addition to any home.

_____ **1.** Many house plants are easy to grow and to maintain.

_____ **2.** Plastic or clay pots are available for plants.

_____ **3.** Plants add beauty, oxygen, and humidity to a house.

_____ **4.** Studies have shown that living with plants calms people down.

_____ **5.** Some African violets have purple blooms.

Outlining ▪ **Organize the following into outline form.**

Topic: Painting Is Hard Work   Sand the surface until smooth

Scrape off the old paint   Preparing the surface

Painting   Spread the paint with even strokes

Stir the paint thoroughly

_____

_____

_____

_____

_____

_____

Revising and Proofreading ▪ Read the paragraph below. Use the proofreader's marks to revise and proofread the paragraph.

Proofreader's Marks

≡	⊙	(sp)
Capitalize.	Add a period.	Correct spelling.
/	⋀	¶
Make a small letter.	Add something.	Indent for new paragraph.
⋀	↶	⟶
Add a comma.	Take something out.	Move something.

---

most people do not know that there are 48 types of eagles in the world people immediately

think of golden eagles and bald eagles two kinds that breed in North america what most

eagles halve in common are large, powerful wings and a sharp beak most eagles return the

to same nest each year and keep the same mates for life. unfortunately, both bald and

golden eagles our declining in population due to extensive hunting by man and loss of

they're natural environment. laws now Protect the eagles.

many types of eagles are the size of hawks. but the large bald eagle and the golden eagle,

with wing spans of about seven feet and body sizes from 30 to 35 inches, are smaller than

the harpy eagle of central and South America. The harpy eagles range from 30 to 37 inches

and live in jungles.

Persuasive Composition ▪ Write a paragraph in which you try to convince the reader that reading throughout life is the best way to continue to learn.

_____

_____

_____

_____

_____

_____

_____

Using the Dictionary ▪ **Use the dictionary samples to answer the questions.**

county (koun′ tē) *n.* **1.** one of the self-governing sections that a state is divided into. **2.** one of the sections that a country is divided into. **3.** the residents of a county. [French *conté*, meaning an area ruled by a count]

mark (märk) *n.* **1.** a line, scratch, or spot left by one object when it touches another object. **2.** a symbol, sign, or inscription. **3.** something, such as a line or object, used as a point of reference. *The rowers passed the half-way mark in record time.* *-v.t.* **1.** to put a mark on. **2.** to be a characteristic of. [Old English, *mearc*, meaning a boundary or sign]

1. Circle the letter of the words that could be the guide words for the above entry.

   a. corn / marine   **b.** courage / mallard   **c.** country / marlin

2. How many definitions are listed for county? _____ mark? _____

3. Write one sentence using the second definition of mark.

   _____

4. Write a sentence using mark as a verb. _____

   _____

5. What part of speech is county? _____

6. How many syllables are in county? _____ mark? _____

7. Write the respelling of county _____ mark _____

8. Which word came from the Old English word mearc? _____

9. Which word's etymology means "a territory ruled by a count"? _____

10. Which word means almost the same in Old English as it does in modern English? _____

Reference Sources ▪ **Write dictionary, encyclopedia, thesaurus, *Readers' Guide,* atlas, or almanac to tell where you would find this information.**

1. _____ the etymology of the word reindeer

2. _____ the history of the Better Business Bureau

3. _____ an antonym for the word hungry

4. _____ the height of Mount Rainier

5. _____ the title of an article on President Clinton

6. _____ the average rainfall in Mexico for the month of July

7. _____ the definitions of the word relate

8. _____ the life of a monarch butterfly

Charts and Graphs ▪ Use the chart and graph to answer the questions.

Movie Viewing Chart

Month	Theater	Rentals
April	53	197
May	117	133
June	201	49
July	185	65
August	178	72

Movie Viewing Graph

Graph Key

Theater _____

Rentals _ _ _ _ _ _ _ _ _ _ _

1. In July, did more people rent movies or go to the theater? _____

2. During which months did more people stay home than go to the theater? _____

3. Is it quicker to determine from the chart or from the graph
   the exact number of families who went to the theater each month? _____

4. Is it quicker to determine from the chart or from the graph how
   the families' movie viewing habits changed over the summer? _____

Visual Aids ▪ Use the map to answer the questions.

1. What is the major resource in Paladin? _____

2. What is the combined yearly value of forest products in Dillon and Cartwright? _____

3. In which state would an oil refinery most likely be found? _____

4. Which state has the widest variety of resources? _____

A. Write S before each pair of synonyms, A before each pair of antonyms, and H before each pair of homonyms.

_____ **1.** distant, far

_____ **2.** jolly, morose

_____ **3.** flee, flea

_____ **4.** sent, scent

B. Write the homograph for the pair of meanings.

1. a. explanation   **b.** a place in a bank for keeping checking or savings _____

C. Write P before each word with a prefix, S before each word with a suffix, and C before each compound word.

_____ **1.** marvelous

_____ **2.** disarming

_____ **3.** waterfront

_____ **4.** foremost

D. Write the two words that make up each contraction.

1. she'd _____   _____

2. didn't _____   _____

E. Underline the word in parentheses that has the more negative connotation.

Our drive to the country was (uneventful, boring).

F. Circle the letter of the idiom that means defends.

1. a. come through   **b.** stands up for

G. Write D before the declarative sentence, IM before the imperative sentence, E before the exclamatory sentence, and IN before the interrogative sentence. Then underline the simple subject, and circle the simple predicate in each sentence.

1. _____ Take that off my chair.

2. _____ Who ate my sandwich?

3. _____ I won the photo contest!

4. _____ I forgot to leave a light on.

H. Write CS before the sentence that has a compound subject and CP before the sentence that has a compound predicate.

1. _____ The whales splashed and slapped the water with their tails.

2. _____ Porpoises and dolphins are not the same.

I. Write CS before the compound sentence. Write RO before the run-on sentence. Write I before the sentence that is in inverted order.

1. _____ I stood in line, but I still didn't get a ticket.

2. _____ It's time to leave, we should say our good-byes.

3. _____ Around the corner came Jerry and Sue.

J. Put brackets around the subordinate clause, and underline the independent clause in this complex sentence. Then write DO over the direct object.

After he had returned, Enrique told Armando the truth.

K. Underline the common nouns, and circle the proper nouns in the sentence.

Before Edward could stop his car, Mr. Huang opened the door and jumped out.

L. Circle the appositive in the sentence. Underline the noun it identifies or explains.

Our local newspaper, *The Hunterstown Gazette*, is the oldest in the state.

M. Write past, present, or future to show the tense of each underlined verb.

1. _____ Yolanda went shopping yesterday.

2. _____ Do you know the answer?

3. _____ It will be dark before he gets here.

4. _____ Rain was predicted for the weekend.

N. Circle the correct verbs in each sentence.

1. It (begun, began) to rain before we (eat, ate).

2. (Learning, Teaching) someone how to rollerblade has (be, been) fun.

3. I (taken, took) my time and (chose, choose) wisely.

4. He (set, sat) his glasses on the table when he (lay, laid) down.

O. Circle the number of the sentence that is in the active voice.

1. James threw the basketball through the hoop.

2. Her brother was expected on the next train.

P. Write SP before the sentence that has a subject pronoun, OP before the sentence that has an object pronoun, PP before the sentence that has a possessive pronoun, and IP before the sentence that has an indefinite pronoun. Circle the pronoun in each sentence.

1. _____ We knew the movie had already begun.

2. _____ Sally told her to hang the clothes in the closet.

3. _____ Stephanie and Frank spent their vacation in Montreal.

4. _____ Someone must have seen where the dog went.

Q. Underline the pronoun. Circle its antecedent.

Annette served the wonderful dinner with her customary flair.

R. On the line before each sentence, write adjective or adverb to describe the underlined word.

1. _____ Jack is the calmest dog I have ever known.

2. _____ The group listened intently to the speech.

3. _____ The bicycle was an antique.

4. _____ He ran faster than anyone else.

5. _____ Her car had two flat tires.

6. _____ The children were exceptionally polite at the dinner.

S. Underline each prepositional phrase twice, and circle each preposition. Underline each conjunction once.

Hoan pretended to be asleep when his father came into his room to wake him for breakfast.

T. Rewrite the letter. Add capital letters and punctuation where needed.

408 greene st
centerville oh 56109
march 15 2006

dear charles

i cant wait until next month ____ its going to be so much fun to finally meet you after all these years of writing ____ i know its still winter in moscow but when you get here itll be springtime ____

Heres what you should bring jeans shirts shorts tennis shoes, and one dressy outfit ____ ive got your schedule memorized and will be waiting at the gate at exactly 1123 ____ are you ready for the time of your life ____ i hope so ____

your friend
sheila

_____

_____

_____

_____

_____

_____

_____

_____

_____

_____

_____

U. Number the sentences in order, with the topic sentence first.

1. _____ The logs are taken by truck to a pulp mill.

2. _____ Then the bark is cut off, and the logs are made into pulp.

3. _____ Finally, the sheets of pulp are heated and dried.

4. _____ Paper is made from trees that have been cut down.

V. Write brainstorming, outlining, or persuading to describe each of the following.

1. bringing to mind as many ideas as possible   _____

2. organizing your thoughts before you write   _____

3. convincing others to accept a personal opinion   _____

Check What You've Learned

W. Rewrite the sentence below. Correct the errors in the sentence by following the proofreader's marks.

judge mayers senteced defendant the to ten years prison inno

_____

society (sə sī'i tē) n. 1. social relationships among humans. 2. a group of humans bound by culture and institutions.

X. Use the dictionary entry to answer the questions.

n.	noun
pron.	pronoun
v.	verb
adj.	adjective
adv.	adverb
prep.	preposition

1. What part of speech is the word society? _____

2. Would social come before or after society? _____

3. Write society separated into syllables. _____

4. Would soak / sock or sod / soft be the guide words for society? _____

Y. Write the letter of the reference source in the blank before its description.

_____ 1. presents information about geographical locations   **a.** *Readers' Guide*

_____ 2. a visual aid that lists information in rows and columns   **b.** thesaurus

_____ 3. a source of articles about many different people and things   **c.** encyclopedia

_____ 4. used to find definitions, pronunciations, and origins of words   **d.** chart

_____ 5. contains information cards on every book in the library   **e.** dictionary

_____ 6. contains specific yearly information on a variety of topics   **f.** card catalog

_____ 7. used to find synonyms and antonyms   **g.** almanac

_____ 8. lists by author and subject articles in magazines   **h.** atlas

Below is a list of the sections on *Check What You've Learned* and the pages on which the skills in each section are taught. If you missed any questions, turn to the pages listed, and practice the skills. Then correct the problems you missed on *Check What You've Learned.*

Section	Practice Page	Section	Practice Page	Section	Practice Page
Unit 1		J	25, 27-30	*Unit 4*	
A	5, 6	*Unit 3*		T	82–90
B	7	K	37		
C	8, 9, 11	L	42	*Unit 5*	
D	10	M	45	U	96–98
E	12	N	46–50, 58–59	V	100–103
F	13	O	54	W	104–105
Unit 2		P	60–62		
G	19, 21	Q	63, 66	*Unit 6*	
H	23	R	67–73	X	110–113
I	22, 29–31	S	74–76	Y	110–113, 115–127

Check What You Know (P. 1)

A. 1. H   **2.** S   **3.** A   **4.** S

B. 1. inch

C. 1. S   **2.** C   **3.** P   **4.** P

D. 1. they have   **2.** we will

E. generous

F. 1. a

G. The words in bold should be circled.

   1. E; (You), **Look**   **3.** IN; you, **are**
   2. IM; (You), **hand**   **4.** D; I, **leave**

H. 1. CS   **2.** CP

I. 1. RO   **2.** CS   **3.** I

J. The doctor handed Jesse the prescription [that he needed]. _(DO marked above "prescription")

Check What You Know (P. 2)

K. The words in bold should be circled.

   Ms. Chang rounded up the group and began the tour of the **Jefferson Memorial**.

L. The words in bold should be circled.

   My favorite uncle, **Tom Fiske**, was recently elected mayor of Greenville.

M. 1. past   **2.** future   **3.** present   **4.** future

N. 1. are, go   **3.** learn, take
   2. sat, laid   **4.** Set, sitting

O. 2 should be circled.

P. The words in bold should be circled.

   1. IP; **Nobody**   **3.** PP; **its**
   2. OP; **him**   **4.** SP; **He**

Q. The word in bold should be circled.

   Janet and Jason met to discuss the response to **their** request.

R. 1. adjective   **4.** adjective
   2. adverb   **5.** adjective
   3. adjective   **6.** adverb

S. The words in bold should be circled.

   I don't have the time or the patience to talk **about** the complaints **of** those people.

Check What You Know (P. 3)

T.
       591 W. Franklin Place
       Bent Tree, TX 78709
       Jan. 27, 2006

Dear Ms. Coleman:

Please know that I called you at exactly 9:15, but nobody answered the phone. I hope that you'll allow me another opportunity to tell you about my work. I have exciting news! I won the national photo contest, and my picture will be in the next issue of Parks of the World.

I look forward to speaking with you. Please call anytime this week between 10:00 and 2:30. I'll be in one of these places: my home, my office, or my car; you have all three numbers.

       Sincerely,
       Eric Flannery

U. 1. 3   **2.** 1   **3.** 2   **4.** 4

V. 1. outlining   **2.** persuading   **3.** brainstorming

Check What You Know (P. 4)

W. As the movie began, the crowd grew silent and concentrated on the action.

X. 1. noun   **3.** Old French   **5.** hon-or
   2. before   **4.** system

Y. 1. h   **3.** f   **5.** e   **7.** c
   2. d   **4.** a   **6.** g   **8.** b

Unit 1   Vocabulary

Lesson 1, Synonyms and Antonyms (P. 5)

A. Discuss your answers with your instructor.

B. Discuss your answers with your instructor.

C. Discuss your answers with your instructor.

D. 1. success   **3.** courageous   **5.** specific
   2. friendly   **4.** unreliable

Lesson 2, Homonyms (P. 6)

A. 1. weight   **8.** loan   **15.** meets
   2. sail   **9.** mist   **16.** rein
   3. browse   **10.** see   **17.** brake
   4. days, inn   **11.** threw, through   **18.** There
   5. floe   **12.** buy, beach   **19.** flew, straight
   6. boulder   **13.** aisle   **20.** allowed
   7. pier   **14.** principal

B. 1. way   **7.** eight   **13.** sea
   2. steel   **8.** vane or vein   **14.** scent or cent
   3. sale   **9.** straight   **15.** pear or pair
   4. fair   **10.** through   **16.** piece
   5. made   **11.** sore   **17.** son
   6. dear   **12.** board   **18.** blew

Lesson 3, Homographs (P. 7)

A. 1. bear   **4.** punch   **7.** ball
   2. jumper   **5.** mum   **8.** pupil
   3. saw   **6.** jar

B. 1. saw   **4.** saw   **7.** jar   **10.** ball
   2. ball   **5.** mum   **8.** pupil
   3. jumper   **6.** punch   **9.** bear

Lesson 4, Prefixes (P. 8)

A. 1. rewrite   **4.** impossible   **7.** impatient
   2. displeased   **5.** uncertain
   3. forewarned   **6.** misspell

B. Discuss your answers with your instructor.

Lesson 5, Suffixes (P. 9)

A. 1. painter   **6.** encouragement
   2. tireless   **7.** fascination
   3. lifelike or lifeless   **8.** childhood
   4. artist   **9.** famous
   5. remarkable

B. 1. reliable
   2. glorious
   3. colorless or colorful or colorist
   4. occasional
   5. fateful or fatal
   6. comfortable or comforter or comfortless
   7. hopeless or hopeful
   8. believable or believer

Lesson 6, Contractions (P. 10)

A. Discuss your answers with your instructor.

B. 1. won't; will not   **6.** can't; cannot
   2. Let's; Let us   **7.** It's; It is
   3. that's; that is   **8.** you're; you are
   4. don't; do not   **9.** We'll; We will or we shall
   5. we'd; we had   **10.** doesn't; does not

Lesson 7, Compound Words (P. 11)

A. Any twelve of the following words should be listed:

sandpaper	paperback	homeroom
homemade	underwater	backwater
fallout	understand	roommate
waterfall	watercolor	playroom
outfield	comeback	playmate
backfield	outcome	playback

B. Discuss your answers with your instructor.

Lesson 8, Connotation/Denotation (P. 12)

A. 1. − ; +   **5.** + ; +   **9.** N; +
   2. + ; −   **6.** + ; N   **10.** − ; +
   3. − ; +   **7.** N; +   **11.** − ; N
   4. + ; −   **8.** + ; −   **12.** − ; +

B. Discuss your answers with your instructor.

Lesson 9, Idioms (P. 13)

A. 1. J   **4.** B   **7.** D or A   **10.** I
   2. C   **5.** K   **8.** H
   3. A or D   **6.** F   **9.** E; G

B. Discuss your answers with your instructor.

Review (P. 14)

A. 1. S   **6.** S   **11.** A   **16.** H   **21.** A
   2. A   **7.** H   **12.** H   **17.** S   **22.** H
   3. S   **8.** S   **13.** S   **18.** H   **23.** A
   4. H   **9.** H   **14.** A   **19.** A   **24.** A
   5. A   **10.** S   **15.** H   **20.** S

B. 1. b   **2.** a   **3.** a   **4.** b

C. 1. preview; see before
   2. nonprofit; not for profit
   3. unusual; not usual
   4. mistaken; wrongly taken

D. 1. thoughtless; without thought
   2. unreadable; not able to be read
   3. unbeatable; not able to be beaten
   4. dangerous; full of danger

Review (P. 15)

E. 1. It is; It's
   2. what is; what's
   3. You have; You've
   4. it would; it'd
   5. should not; shouldn't
   6. I would; I'd

F. 1. forehead; front of the head
   2. Everything; every single thing
   3. newsstand; stand where news materials are sold
   4. roommate; one who shares lodging
   5. underwater; under the water
   6. supermarket; large market that sells food and household items

G. 1. brilliant   **3.** thrifty   **5.** graceful
   2. helpful   **4.** gulp

H. 1. make ends meet; have enough money
   2. turning over a new leaf; changing one's ways
   3. skating on thin ice; taking a chance
   4. ran into; encountered
   5. all ears; listened carefully

Using What You've Learned (P. 16)

A.
1. marvelous
2. rethink
3. forceful
4. pianist
5. adjustable
6. impossible
7. forefront
8. personal

B.
1. group
2. walked
3. asked
4. fragile
5. fragrance
6. tasty
7. golden
8. confident
9. wrote
10. soiled
11. leaned
12. brave

Using What You've Learned (P. 17)

C. Checks should be placed on the following blanks:

1. X
2. X
3.
4. X
5. X
6. X
7.
8. X

D. Checks should be placed on the following blanks:

1. X
2. X
3. X
4. X
5. X
6. X
7. X
8. X

Unit 2 Sentences

Lesson 10, Recognizing Sentences (P. 18)

S should precede the following sentences, and students should end each with a period: 2, 5, 6, 7, 9, 11, 12, 14, 17, 18, 19, 20, 22, 23, 26, 27, 30.

Lesson 11, Types of Sentences (P. 19)

1. IN; ?
2. IN: ?
3. IM: .
4. D; .
5. E; !
6. IN; ?
7. IM; .
8. D; .
9. E; !
10. IM; .
11. D; .
12. D; . or E; !
13. IN; ?
14. IN; ?
15. IM: .
16. D; .
17. IM; .
18. D; .
19. IN; ?
20. D; .
21. IM; .
22. IN; ?
23. D; .
24. IM; . or E; !
25. IN; ?

Lesson 12, Complete Subjects and Predicates (P. 20)

1. An earthquake/formed…
2. The deepest places in the oceans/are…
3. The seasons/are…
4. Many of the people/waited…
5. The two mechanics/have…
6. The first telegraph line/was…
7. The territory of Iowa/was…
8. The origin of the wheat plant/is…
9. The television tube/was…
10. The shortest day of the year/is…
11. Workers/dicussed…
12. Fossils/show…
13. Great deposits of bauxite, from which aluminum is extracted,/exist…
14. The Shoshone/live…
15. The citizens of Georgia/built…
16. Who/originated…
17. Many people/watched…
18. Mexican silver mines/were…
19. A steamboat/was…
20. Who/brought…
21. Benjamin Franklin/was…
22. All of the guests/enjoyed…
23. Annapolis Academy/was…
24. The three cities that we visited/were…
25. Banff National Park/is…
26. Many towns in the United States/are…

Lesson 13, Simple Subjects and Predicates (P. 21)

1. The different meanings for that word/cover…
2. A valuable oil/is made…
3. A beautiful highway/winds…
4. The woman in the black dress/studied…
5. The meadowlark/builds…
6. The making of ice cream/can be…
7. Many stories/have been written…
8. His answer to the question/was incorrect.
9. Every sentence/should begin…
10. The rotation of the earth on its axis/causes…
11. In Norway, a narrow inlet of the sea between cliffs/is called…
12. The Dutch/cultivated…
13. The two treasury mints in the United States/ are located…
14. Benjamin Franklin's *Poor Richard's Almanac*/is…
15. The warm climate of Jamaica/attracts…
16. That movie/has been shown…
17. Acres of wheat/rippled…
18. That mechanic/completed…
19. The people in that picture/were boarding…
20. One/can find…

21. The <u>city</u> of Albuquerque/<u><u>is</u></u>…
22. The apple <u>trees</u>/<u><u>have</u></u>…
23. <u>Sequoias</u>, the world's tallest trees,/<u><u>are found</u></u>…
24. <u>John Banister</u>/<u><u>was</u></u>…
25. The tall pine <u>trees</u>/<u><u>hide</u></u>…
26. The <u>woman</u>/<u><u>filled</u></u>…

Lesson 14, Position of Subjects (P. 22)

1. The <u>movie</u> <u><u>is playing</u></u> when?
2. <u>I</u> <u><u>will</u></u> never <u><u>forget</u></u> my first train trip.
3. The <u>picture</u> <u>I</u> want to buy <u><u>is</u></u> here.
4. <u>He</u> <u><u>has</u></u> seldom <u><u>been</u></u> ill.
5. The <u>lights</u> <u><u>went</u></u> out.
6. <u>Bookcases</u> <u><u>were</u></u> on all sides of the room.
7. <u>You</u> <u><u>take</u></u> the roast from the oven.
8. The speeding <u>car</u> <u><u>swerved</u></u> around the sharp curve.
9. <u>You</u> <u><u>get</u></u> out of the swimming pool.
10. <u>You</u> <u><u>study</u></u> for the spelling test.
11. Two <u>children</u> <u><u>are</u></u> in the pool.

Lesson 15, Compound Subjects and Predicates (P. 23)

A. 1. <u>Lewis</u> and <u>Clark</u>/<u><u>blazed</u></u> a trail across the North American continent.
2. The <u>rose</u> and the <u>jasmine</u>/<u><u>are</u></u> important flowers for perfume manufacturing.
3. <u>Kelly</u> and <u>Amy</u>/<u><u>went</u></u> with us.
4. <u>Chris</u>/<u><u>swept</u></u> the floor, <u><u>dusted</u></u> the furniture, and <u><u>washed</u></u> the windows.
5. <u>Empires</u>/<u><u>flourish</u></u> and <u><u>decay</u></u>.
6. The level of the <u>lake</u>/<u><u>rises</u></u> and <u><u>falls</u></u> several times each year.
7. <u>Juanita</u> and her <u>brother</u>/<u><u>are</u></u> excellent skaters.
8. <u>Dwight D. Eisenhower</u> and <u>Douglas MacArthur</u>/<u><u>were</u></u> famous American generals.
9. <u>He</u>/<u><u>turned</u></u> slowly and then <u><u>answered</u></u> my question.
10. <u>Museums</u>, <u>libraries</u>, and art <u>galleries</u>/<u><u>are found</u></u> in many cities.
11. The <u>typewriters</u>, the <u>desks</u>, and the <u>chairs</u>/<u><u>are</u></u> all new.
12. The <u>plants</u>/<u><u>grew</u></u> tall and <u><u>flowered</u></u>.
13. <u>Stephanie</u> and <u>Teresa</u>/<u><u>worked</u></u> hard.
14. <u>He</u>/<u><u>ran</u></u> and <u><u>slid</u></u> into third base.
15. The sales <u>clerk</u>/<u><u>added</u></u> up the numbers and <u><u>wrote</u></u> down the total.
16. <u>Reading</u> and <u>baking</u>/<u><u>are</u></u> her favorite pastimes.
17. <u>Mary</u>/<u><u>drank</u></u> iced tea and <u><u>ate</u></u> a sandwich.
18. <u>Cars</u> and <u>trucks</u>/<u><u>sped</u></u> past.
19. <u>Red</u> and <u>blue</u>/<u><u>are</u></u> his favorite colors.

B. Discuss your answers with your instructor.

C. Discuss your answers with your instructor.

Lesson 16, Combining Sentences (P. 24)

Sentences may vary. Suggested:

1. The nine planets in our solar system <u>vary</u> in size and <u>are</u> at different distances from the sun.
2. Mercury and Venus do not <u>have</u> any moons.
3. Venus is similar in some ways to the earth but <u>is</u> much hotter than the earth.
4. Pluto is the farthest planet from the sun and <u>takes</u> 248 years to revolve around the sun.
5. Planets <u>revolve</u> around the sun in regular paths and also <u>rotate</u> and <u>spin</u> like tops.
6. Mercury and Venus revolve around the sun in less than a year.
7. The solar system <u>may have been formed</u> in a collision between the sun and another star or <u>may have come</u> from a cloud of gas.

Lesson 17, Direct Objects (P. 25)

1. Juanita's good driving <u>prevented</u> an ^{DO}<u>accident</u>.
2. Every person <u>should have</u> an ^{DO}<u>appreciation</u> of music.
3. Gene, <u>pass</u> the ^{DO}<u>potatoes</u>, please.
4. Do not <u>waste</u> your ^{DO}<u>time</u> on this project.
5. James, <u>did</u> you <u>keep</u> those ^{DO}<u>coupons</u>?
6. Geraldo <u>collects</u> foreign ^{DO}<u>stamps</u>.
7. Eli Whitney <u>invented</u> the cotton ^{DO}<u>gin</u>.
8. <u>Answer</u> my ^{DO}<u>question</u>.
9. We <u>are picking</u> ^{DO}<u>trophies</u> for our bowling league.
10. Who <u>invented</u> the ^{DO}<u>steamboat</u>?
11. I <u>am reading</u> Hemingway's ^{DO}<u>*The Old Man and the Sea*</u>.
12. The North Star <u>guides</u> ^{DO}<u>sailors</u>.
13. The Phoenicians <u>gave</u> the ^{DO}<u>alphabet</u> to civilization.
14. Every person <u>should study</u> world ^{DO}<u>history</u>.
15. Who <u>made</u> this ^{DO}<u>cake</u>?
16. Can you <u>find</u> a direct ^{DO}<u>object</u> in this sentence?
17. Who <u>wrote</u> the ^{DO}<u>story</u> of Johnny Tremain?
18. We <u>bought</u> several ^{DO}<u>curios</u> for our friends.
19. Tamara <u>read</u> the ^{DO}<u>minutes</u> of our last club meeting.
20. Did you ever <u>make</u> a time ^{DO}<u>budget</u> of your own?
21. Mountains <u>have</u> often <u>affected</u> the ^{DO}<u>history</u> of a nation.
22. Emma and Joe <u>baked</u> a ^{DO}<u>pie</u>.

Lesson 18, Indirect Objects (P. 26)

1. The pitcher threw David a fast ball.
   (IO = David, DO = ball)
2. We gave the usher our tickets.
   (IO = usher, DO = tickets)
3. The doctor handed Chris the prescription.
   (IO = Chris, DO = prescription)
4. Mr. Lewis sold us a set of encyclopedias.
   (IO = us, DO = set)
5. Have you written Andrea the time of our arrival?
   (IO = Andrea, DO = time)
6. The supervisor paid the employee a high salary.
   (IO = employee, DO = salary)
7. Experience should teach us wisdom.
   (IO = us, DO = wisdom)
8. Who sent Amy that long letter?
   (IO = Amy, DO = letter)
9. Maria, show us that magic trick.
   (IO = us, DO = trick)
10. I gave the cashier the money for our tickets.
    (IO = cashier, DO = money)
11. Many years ago, a clever writer gave us the story of Robinson Crusoe.
    (IO = us, DO = story)
12. A guide always shows visitors the interesting things in this museum.
    (IO = visitors, DO = things)
13. Working crossword puzzles gives many people hours of enjoyment.
    (IO = people, DO = hours)
14. Carlos, give the group a lecture on saving money.
    (IO = group, DO = lecture)
15. The study of space travel has brought us many new inventions.
    (IO = us, DO = inventions)
16. Dale, please take Sandra these books.
    (IO = Sandra, DO = books)
17. Mrs. Yonge gave Joanne several plants.
    (IO = Joanne, DO = plants)
18. Please give me a drink of water.
    (IO = me, DO = drink)
19. Who gave the United States flag the name of Old Glory?
    (IO = flag, DO = name)
20. Will you give me those instructions again?
    (IO = me, DO = instructions)

Lesson 19, Independent and Subordinate Clauses (P. 27)

A. 1. We arrived late because we couldn't find the theater.
   2. The play started before we found our seats.
   3. We got one of the special programs that were being sold.
   4. When the play was over, the audience applauded.
   5. After we saw the show, we went for a walk.

6. Although the night was cool, the walk was enjoyable.
7. While we were walking, I noticed the moon.
8. Since it was a full moon, it was shining brightly.
9. We walked along the lake until it became very late.
10. By the time I got home, it was almost midnight.

B. 1. Japan is a country where some trains travel at very fast speeds.
   2. The airplane that we saw can land in only a few airports in this country.
   3. Henry Hudson discovered the river that bears his name.
   4. When you respect others, you win respect for yourself.
   5. Diego found the new job that was perfect for him.
   6. Colleen is the one who was elected without a run-off.
   7. The coin that I purchased is an old French crown.
   8. When I awoke, it was broad daylight.
   9. Those who would control others must first control themselves.
   10. The camel is the only pack animal that can stand the test of the Sahara.

Lesson 20, Adjective and Adverb Clauses (P. 28)

A. 1. adjective; whose bravery won many victories
   2. adjective; who reads the most books
   3. adverb; because he hadn't set the alarm
   4. adverb; when our team comes off the field
   5. adjective; that he hears
   6. adjective; that we planned

B. Discuss your answers with your instructor.

Lesson 21, Compound and Complex Sentences (P. 29)

A. 1. CP   7. CX   13. CX   19. CX
   2. CP   8. CX   14. CX   20. CP
   3. CX   9. CP   15. CP   21. CX
   4. CP   10. CP   16. CP   22. CP
   5. CX   11. CP   17. CX   23. CP
   6. CP   12. CX   18. CX   24. CX

Lesson 21, Compound and Complex Sentences (P. 30)

B. 1. [The streets are filled with cars], but [the sidewalks are empty.]
   2. [Those apples are too sour to eat,] but [those pears are perfect.]
   3. [She studies hard,] but [she saves some time to enjoy herself.]
   4. [They lost track of time], so [they were late.]
   5. [Eric had not studied,] so [he failed the test.]

6. [Yesterday it rained all day,] but [today the sun is shining.]

7. [I set the alarm to get up early,] but [I couldn't get up.]

8. [They may sing and dance until dawn,] but [they will be exhausted.]

9. [My friend moved to Texas,] and [I will miss her.]

10. [They arrived at the theater early,] but [there was still a long line.]

11. [Lisa took her dog to the veterinarian,] but [his office was closed.]

12. [The black cat leaped,] but [fortunately it didn't catch the bird.]

13. [I found a baseball in the bushes,] and [I gave it to my brother.]

14. [We loaded the cart with groceries,] and [we went to the checkout.]

15. [The stadium was showered with lights,] but [the stands were empty.]

16. [The small child whimpered,] and [her mother hugged her.]

17. [The dark clouds rolled in,] and [then it began to rain.]

C. 1. The hummingbird is the only bird that can fly backward.
2. The cat that is sitting in the window is mine.
3. The car that is parked outside is new.
4. Jack, who is a football star, is class president.
5. Bonnie, who is an artist, is also studying computer science.
6. John likes food that is cooked in the microwave.
7. The composer who wrote the music comes from Germany.
8. We missed seeing him because we were late.
9. When Jake arrives, we will tell him what happened.
10. She walked slowly because she had hurt her leg.
11. When she walked to the podium, everyone applauded.
12. If animals could talk, they might have a lot to tell.
13. Many roads that were built in our city are no longer traveled.
14. My address book, which is bright red, is gone.
15. Ann, who is from Georgia, just started working here today.
16. The crowd cheered when the player came to bat.
17. When he hit the ball, everyone cheered.

Lesson 22, Correcting Run-on Sentences (P. 31)

Sentences may vary. Suggested:

1. The brain is surrounded by three membranes. The skull encloses the brain and these three membranes.
2. The brain reaches its full size by the time a person is twenty, and at that time, it weighs about three pounds.
3. The brain helps a person see, hear, touch, smell, and taste. It also makes it possible for one to remember and forget, talk and write, and feel emotions.
4. The brain has three main parts. These parts are the cerebrum, the cerebellum, and the brain stem.
5. A computer is like a human brain. However, computers cannot perform all the functions of the human brain.

Lesson 23, Expanding Sentences (P. 32)

A. Discuss your answers with your instructor.

B. Discuss your answers with your instructor.

Review (P. 33)

A.
1. IN; ?   4. E; !   7. D; .   10. IN; ?
2. IM; .   5. IN; ?   8. D; .
3. D; .   6. IM: .   9. D; .

B. 1. The leaves on the trees in the park turned orange and yellow.
2. The tourists came to see the changing colors.
3. The children gathered the leaves.
4. Some artists painted the colorful scene.
5. Camera buffs snapped photographs.
6. Dogs jumped and rolled in the piles of crackling leaves.
7. Adults and children were delighted by the scene.
8. A toddler handed his mother a bright orange leaf.
9. She happily took the leaf.
10. Then she gave him a hug.

C. 1. The crowd of protesting citizens/marched down the street.
2. Kara/felt the first drops of rain on her face.
3. Under the fence crawled/ the frightened coyote.
4. All the patrol cars/are parked near the police station.

D. 1. The leaves of some trees turn bright colors and fall off in the autumn.
2. Linda and Judy refuse to watch violent movies.
3. Tom washed and waxed his car.
4. James, Kathryn, and Kamal ride to work together.

Review (P. 34)

E. 1. After the first act ended, we left the theater.
2. Pat used her computer for the design that won the contest.
3. By the way they were talking, we knew they weren't going.
4. Canada and the United States share a long border that runs east and west.

F. 1. I was at the station <u>when the train arrived</u>.
  2. The letter <u>that she found</u> had been mailed two years earlier.
  3. <u>After he lit the charcoal</u>, he put on the steaks.
  4. The heel broke off her shoe <u>while she was walking</u>.

G. 1. who writes the funniest limerick; adjective
  2. because she wasn't paying attention; adverb
  3. when the judge enters the courtroom; adverb
  4. that she wore to the dance; adjective

H. 1. CX **2.** CP **3.** CX **4.** CX **5.** CX

I. Sentences may vary. Suggested:
  1. Janet brought the DVD to my house, and I popped it into the DVD player.
  2. Teresa went to the party. She took salad, and it was good.
  3. What was in the salad? It contained fresh fruits and walnuts.
  4. She gave me the recipe. I can copy it for you.

Using What You've Learned (P. 35)

A. 1. B **7.** C
  2. A **8.** D
  3. D, E **9.** The continuous noise
  4. E **10.** noise
  5. E **11.** go off day and night
  6. A, B **12.** go

B. The words in bold should be circled.
  1. We planned this trip a month ago, **after the holidays were over**.
  2. **After we planned the trip**, <u>we posted a sign-up sheet</u>.
  3. <u>Here is the sign-up sheet</u> **that was hanging in the club room**.
  4. <u>Everyone</u> **who is in the ski club** <u>plans to take the trip</u>.
  5. **When everyone packs carefully**, <u>the ski gear fits on the bus</u>.
  6. **When the bus arrives**, <u>we will hand out the tickets</u>.

C. Sentences may vary. Suggested:
  1. It is sunny out today, yet it's still too cold to go to the beach.
  2. Maria can't go with us today, but she can come tomorrow.
  3. Carol said she would meet us, so I'll tell her we aren't going.
  4. We could go to see that adventure movie, or we could go see the new exhibit.

Using What You've Learned (P. 36)

D. 1. The news of the storm was reported on a television bulletin.
  2. The small airplane taxied into the hangar.
  3. The tired passengers came down the ramp.

E. Discuss your answers with your instructor.

F. Paragraphs may vary. Suggested:

  In space medicine research, new types of miniature equipment for checking how the body functions have been developed. On the spacecraft, astronauts' breathing rates, heartbeats, and blood pressure are taken with miniature devices no larger than a pill. These devices detect the information and transmit it to scientists back on Earth. They allow the scientists to monitor astronauts' body responses from a long distance and over long periods of time.

G. Discuss your answers with your instructor.

Unit 3 — Grammar and Usage

Lesson 24, Common and Proper Nouns (P. 37)

A. Proper nouns are in bold. Common nouns are underlined. P should be written above the proper nouns and C should be written above the common nouns.
  1. **Maria** is my sister.
  2. **Honolulu** is the chief <u>city</u> and <u>capital</u> of **Hawaii**.
  3. **Rainbow Natural Bridge** is hidden away in the wild mountainous <u>part</u> of southern **Utah**.
  4. **The Declaration of Independence** is often called the birth <u>certificate</u> of the **United States**.
  5. **Abraham Lincoln**, **Edgar Allan Poe**, and **Frederic Chopin** were born in the same <u>year</u>.

B. Discuss your answers with your instructor.

C. Discuss your answers with your instructor.

Lesson 25, Concrete, Abstract, and Collective Nouns (P. 38)

1. abstract	**15.** collective	**29.** collective
2. abstract	**16.** abstract	**30.** concrete
3. collective	**17.** concrete	**31.** collective
4. abstract	**18.** collective	**32.** abstract
5. collective	**19.** concrete	**33.** collective
6. concrete	**20.** abstract	**34.** concrete
7. collective	**21.** collective	**35.** collective
8. collective	**22.** collective	**36.** abstract
9. concrete	**23.** concrete	**37.** concrete
10. collective	**24.** abstract	**38.** concrete
11. abstract	**25.** collective	**39.** abstract
12. collective	**26.** collective	**40.** concrete
13. abstract	**27.** concrete	**41.** abstract
14. concrete	**28.** abstract	**42.** abstract

Lesson 26, Singular and Plural Nouns (P. 39)

A.
1. counties
2. ponies
3. tomatoes
4. banjos
5. matches
6. windows
7. centuries
8. trenches
9. bookcases
10. videos
11. radios
12. farms
13. flies
14. heroes
15. dresses
16. boots
17. desks
18. daisies

Lesson 26, Singular and Plural Nouns (P. 40)

B.
1. mouthful
2. proof
3. 6
4. calf
5. knife
6. Jones
7. child
8. goose
9. wolf
10. roof
11. gentleman
12. editor-in-chief
13. +
14. cupful
15. trout
16. mouse

C.
1. boxes
2. cities
3. deer
4. flashes
5. coaches
6. churches
7. potatoes
8. *e*'s
9. O'Keefes
10. fish
11. scarves
12. *n*'s
13. radios
14. oxen
15. pilots
16. 90's
17. women
18. *i*'s

Lesson 27, Possessive Nouns (P. 41)

1. Steve's
2. mother's
3. friends'
4. woman's
5. collector's
6. Rosa's; child's
7. Warrens'
8. vice-president's
9. mayor's
10. Tony's
11. women's
12. family's
13. day's
14. lifeguards'
15. team's
16. children's
17. Juan's
18. Jim's
19. Calvin's
20. Lees'
21. Mark's
22. Frank's; Jean's
23. neighbors'
24. Masons'
25. States'

Lesson 28, Appositives (P. 42)

The words in bold should be circled.

1. **Jan Matzeliger**, the inventor of the first shoemaking machine, was born in South America.
2. **Niagara Falls**, the waterfalls in New York, is not the tallest in the country.
3. **Harvard**, the oldest university in the United States, is in Massachusetts.
4. My **brother** Jim lives in Connecticut.
5. **Diane Feinstein**, a mayor of San Francisco, was San Francisco's first woman mayor.
6. **The Sears Tower**, one of the tallest buildings in the world, is in Chicago.
7. Scott's **cousin** Liz sells antique cars.
8. **Leontyne Price**, the opera singer, was born in Mississippi.
9. The Pilgrim's **ship** the Mayflower had a stormy voyage.
10. Tom's **dog** Jasmine likes to swim.
11. **Dr. Miller**, our family physician, is attending a convention with her husband.
12. The **swimmer** Mark Spitz won seven gold medals in one Olympics.
13. **Fort Worth**, a city in Texas, is almost midway between the Atlantic and the Pacific.
14. **Aunt Lee**, my father's sister, is coming to visit.
15. **Mr. Diddon**, coach of the hockey team, has never had a losing season.
16. **Monticello**, Jefferson's home, is an example of colonial architecture.
17. The **inventor** Thomas Edison is responsible for many electrical breakthroughs.
18. **Athens**, the leading city of ancient Greece, was a center of culture.
19. The Aztec **king** Montezuma was captured by Cortez.
20. The boll **weevil**, a small beetle, causes great damage to cotton.
21. The **Hoover Dam**, a dam in the Colorado River, took five years to build.
22. **Antares**, a star many times larger than the sun, is the red star in Scorpio.
23. The **composer** Mozart lived a short but productive life.
24. That is a **copperhead**, one of the four poisonous snakes found in the United States.
25. **Mt. McKinley**, a rugged mountain, is the tallest mountain in North America.

Lesson 29, Verbs (P. 43)

1. is scattering; scattered; (have, had, has) scattered
2. is expressing; expressed; (have, had, has) expressed
3. is painting; painted; (have, had, has) painted
4. is calling; called; (have, had, has) called
5. is cooking; cooked; (have, had, has) cooked
6. is observing; observed; (have, had, has) observed
7. is looking; looked; (have, had, has) looked
8. is walking; walked; (have, had, has) walked
9. is rambling; rambled; (have, had, has) rambled
10. is shouting; shouted; (have, had, has) shouted
11. is noticing; noticed; (have, had, has) noticed
12. is ordering; ordered; (have, had, has) ordered
13. is gazing; gazed; (have, had, has) gazed
14. is borrowing; borrowed; (have, had, has) borrowed
15. is starting; started; (have, had, has) started
16. is working; worked; (have, had, has) worked

Lesson 30, Verb Phrases (P. 44)

A. The words in bold should be circled.

1. Most people **have** heard the story of Jonathan Chapman.
2. He **was** born in 1775 and **has** become an American legend.
3. You **may have** heard of him as the barefooted, lovable Johnny Appleseed.
4. As Jonathan Chapman, he **had** grown up in the woods near Boston, Massachusetts.
5. He **had** learned about fruit trees in the orchards near his family's farm.
6. He **was** always interested in the stories he **had** heard about the Great West.
7. As a young man, he **had** declared, "I **will** go west to Pennsylvania and plant my own orchard."
8. Jonathan **had** done just that, but in a few years, the wilderness **had** moved farther west.
9. "What **should** I do now?" Jonathan asked himself.
10. "I **will** plant other apple orchards!" was his answer.
11. Jonathan **could** not remain content.
12. Soon he **was** traveling with the other settlers as the frontier pushed farther and farther west.
13. People called him Johnny Appleseed, that odd man who **did** not have a home.
14. He **would** sleep out in the open with his beloved trees.

B. Discuss your answers with your instructor.

Lesson 31, Verb Tenses (P. 45)

1. brought; past
2. know; present
3. will close; future
4. will continue; future
5. has donated; present perfect
6. had told; past perfect
7. was; past
8. sings; present
9. will have paid; future perfect
10. will have been; future perfect
11. had been playing; past perfect
12. have anchored; present perfect

Lesson 32, Using Irregular Verbs (P. 46)

A.
1. (is) doing; did; (has) done
2. (is) coming; came; (has) come
3. (is) eating; ate; (has) eaten
4. (is) going; went; (has) gone
5. (is) seeing; saw; (has) seen
6. (is) taking; took; (has) taken

B.
1. seen	7. going	13. taking
2. seen	8. eaten	14. come
3. taking	9. gone	15. eaten
4. seen	10. taking	16. seen
5. eaten	11. did	17. came or come
6. gone	12. done	18. did

Lesson 32, Using Irregular Verbs (P. 47)

C.
1. is beginning; began; has begun
2. is drinking; drank; has drunk
3. is driving; drove; has driven
4. is giving; gave; has given
5. is running; ran; has run

D.
1. gave or is giving	11. began
2. ran or are running	12. given
3. begun	13. beginning
4. began	14. ran
5. drunk	15. given
6. driven	16. gave
7. given	17. begun
8. beginning	18. drunk
9. run	19. began
10. ran or is running	20. running

Lesson 32, Using Irregular Verbs (P. 48)

E.
1. is growing; grew; has grown
2. is knowing; knew; has known
3. is ringing; rang; has rung
4. is singing; sang; has sung
5. is speaking; spoke; has spoken

F.
1. sung	8. spoke	15. thrown
2. grew	9. rang	16. grown
3. knew	10. spoken	17. known
4. grown	11. speaking	18. growing
5. singing	12. sang	19. rang
6. rung	13. known	20. spoken
7. grown	14. rang	

Lesson 32, Using Irregular Verbs (P. 49)

G.
1. is blowing; blew; has blown
2. is breaking; broke; has broken
3. is choosing; chose; has chosen
4. is drawing; drew; has drawn
5. is flying; flew; has flown

H. Answers may vary for numbers 2, 4, 7 and 10. Suggested:

1. drawn	8. broken	15. froze
2. blew	9. choosing	16. chosen
3. flying	10. drew	17. broke
4. chose	11. broken	18. drawn
5. chosen	12. broke	19. breaking
6. blown	13. chosen	20. drawn
7. broke	14. broke	

Lesson 32, Using Irregular Verbs (P. 50)

I.
1. is becoming; became; has become
2. is falling; fell; has fallen
3. is riding; rode; has ridden
4. is rising; rose; has risen
5. is stealing; stole; has stolen
6. is showing; showed; has shown
7. is sinking; sank; has sunk
8. is swimming; swam; has swum
9. is tearing; tore; has torn
10. is wearing; wore; has worn

J.
1. ridden
2. risen
3. wore
4. stolen
5. riding
6. swimming
7. tore
8. sank
9. stolen
10. ridden
11. worn
12. worn
13. rose
14. risen
15. fallen

Lesson 33, Mood (P. 51)

1. imperative
2. indicative
3. subjunctive
4. imperative
5. indicative
6. indicative
7. indicative
8. subjunctive
9. imperative
10. subjunctive
11. imperative
12. imperative
13. indicative
14. subjunctive
15. indicative
16. indicative
17. subjunctive
18. imperative
19. subjunctive

Lesson 34, Transitive and Intransitive Verbs (P. 52)

A.
1. walked; intransitive
2. is; intransitive
3. Move; transitive
4. listened; intransitive
5. wore; transitive
6. built; transitive
7. is; intransitive
8. lives; intransitive
9. elected; transitive
10. paid; transitive
11. send; transitive
12. is; intransitive
13. drew; transitive
14. study; intransitive
15. cried; intransitive
16. made; transitive
17. ran; intransitive
18. learned; transitive
19. barked; intransitive
20. bring; transitive
21. baked; transitive

Lesson 34, Transitive and Intransitive Verbs (P. 53)

B.
1. signed; transitive
2. repaired; transitive
3. shipped; transitive
4. may cause; transitive
5. was; intransitive
6. has; transitive
7. Explain; transitive
8. whistled; intransitive
9. blocked; transitive
10. have dropped; intransitive
11. change; transitive
12. attracts; transitive
13. was; intransitive
14. has; transitive
15. invented; transitive
16. cooked; transitive
17. discovered; transitive
18. traveled; intransitive
19. composed; transitive
20. was; intransitive
21. destroyed; transitive
22. exercises; intransitive
23. talked; intransitive
24. Have seen; transitive
25. cause; transitive
26. is studying; intransitive
27. bought; transitive

Lesson 35, Active and Passive Voice (P. 54)

1. was invented; passive
2. hit; active
3. was rung; passive
4. was thrown; passive
5. has bought; active
6. was announced; passive
7. blamed; active
8. were selected; passive
9. typed; active
10. stated; active
11. flopped; active
12. were written; passive
13. gave; active
14. held; active
15. has bought; active
16. was broken; passive
17. shook; active
18. was carried; passive
19. was given; passive
20. wrote; active

Lesson 36, Gerunds (P. 55)

1. living
2. fighting
3. Landing
4. Climbing
5. moaning
6. barking
7. Keeping
8. hanging
9. Laughing
10. Being
11. Making
12. Winning
13. pitching
14. eating
15. Playing
16. Planning
17. packing
18. howling
19. doing
20. living
21. planting; hunting; fishing
22. writing
23. skating
24. boating
25. Pressing
26. mapping
27. Swimming
28. driving

Lesson 37, Infinitives (P. 56)

1. to go	11. to be	22. To succeed
2. to see	12. to travel	23. to see
3. to serve	13. to play	24. to eat
4. To shoot	14. to rise	25. to see
5. to walk	15. to see	26. to have; to be
6. to stand; to sit; to walk; to dance	16. to enter	27. to receive
	17. to mail	28. To score
7. to use; to make	18. To cook	29. to go
8. to get	19. to meet	30. to paint
9. to make	20. to speak	
10. to clean	21. to exhibit	

Lesson 38, Participles (P. 57)

1. running	11. produced	21. Teasing
2. showing	12. burdened	22. lifting
3. scampering	13. thinking	23. chirping
4. hidden	14. injured	24. surviving
5. advancing	15. expanding	25. dedicated
6. Biting	16. fanned	26. Homing
7. falling	17. shoving	27. whistling
8. whispering	18. frozen	28. Ironed
9. preparing	19. playing	29. standing
10. enjoying	20. cleaned	30. loving

Lesson 39, Using *Lie/Lay* (P. 58)

A.
1. lies	4. lie	7. lain	10. lies	13. lies
2. Lay	5. laid	8. lie	11. lain	
3. lying	6. laid	9. laid	12. lay	

B. Discuss your answers with your instructor.

Lesson 40, Using *Sit/Set* and *Learn/Teach* (P. 59)

1. set	9. teach	17. teach
2. teaching	10. sit	18. sit
3. learn	11. teach; learn	19. taught
4. sit	12. sat	20. taught
5. sitting	13. set	21. set
6. teach	14. teach	22. set
7. sit	15. set	23. teaching
8. sat	16. taught	24. sitting

Lesson 41, Pronouns (P. 60)

1. you; my	14. They; us; them
2. you; me; I; them	15. she
3. you; me; our	16. he; you
4. I; you	17. She; us
5. We; him	18. I
6. me	19. your
7. We; they; us	20. me
8. She; me	21. you; our
9. She; you; me; her	22. I; you; my; you; it
10. We; them	23. I; him; my; we; her
11. we; our	24. they; us; their
12. He; their	25. Your; your
13. She; my	26. us; her; our

Lesson 42, Using *Its* and *It's* (P. 61)

A.
1. its	6. It's	11. it's	16. It's
2. It's	7. It's	12. its	17. its
3. it's	8. It's; its	13. its	18. its
4. It's	9. its	14. it's	19. it's
5. it's	10. It's	15. its	20. its

B. Discuss your answers with your instructor.

C. Discuss your answers with your instructor.

Lesson 43, Demonstrative and Indefinite Pronouns (P. 62)

A.
1. Those	7. This	13. those
2. That	8. these	14. These
3. these	9. These	15. that
4. This; that	10. this	16. that
5. those	11. those	
6. that	12. this	

B.
1. Both	7. Some	13. Each
2. each	8. each	14. Some
3. Several	9. anyone	15. someone
4. some	10. someone	16. Everybody
5. Everyone	11. Both	
6. someone	12. One	

Lesson 44, Antecedents (P. 63)

The words in bold should be circled.

1. **Everyone**; his or her	14. **woman**; her
2. **Each**; his or her	15. **one**; his or her
3. **Sophia**; her	16. **Joseph**; his
4. **I**; my	17. **man**; his
5. **members**; their	18. **waiters**; their
6. **women**; their	19. **student**; his or her
7. **Someone**; her or his	20. **person**; her or his
8. **each**; his or her	21. **man**; his
9. **Joanne**; her	22. **woman**; her
10. **woman**; her	23. **Jeff and Tom**; their
11. **anyone**; his or her	24. **Cliff**; he
12. **student**; his or her	25. **bird**; its
13. **I**; my	26. **Mark**; his

Lesson 45, Relative Pronouns (P. 64)

The words in bold should be circled.

1. **letter**; that	14. **hamburgers**; that
2. **Karen**; who	15. **food**; that
3. **Robert Burns**; who	16. **painting**; that
4. **Sylvia**; who	17. **sweater**; that
5. **shop**; that	18. **one**; whom
6. **farmhouse**; that	19. **money**; that
7. **pearl**; that	20. **person**; who
8. **bridge**; which	21. **animal**; that
9. **animal**; that	22. **guests**; whom
10. **regions**; that	23. **file**; which
11. **turkey**; that	24. **artist**; whose
12. **story**; which	25. **attraction**; that
13. **person**; whom	26. **writer**; whom

Lesson 46, Using *Who/Whom* (P. 65)

1. Who
2. Who
3. Whom
4. Who
5. Who
6. Who
7. whom
8. whom
9. Who
10. whom
11. Whom
12. Whom
13. whom
14. Who
15. Whom
16. whom
17. whom
18. Whom
19. Who
20. Whom
21. Who

Lesson 47, Using Pronouns (P. 66)

1. I
2. He; I
3. that
4. he; she
5. me
6. who
7. Whom
8. me
9. whom
10. me
11. whom
12. her; me
13. she; him
14. who
15. those
16. she
17. me
18. his or her
19. me
20. Those
21. me
22. him
23. These
24. he
25. he
26. Those
27. me
28. he
29. whom
30. their
31. Who
32. she
33. his or her
34. who

Lesson 48, Adjectives (P. 67)

A.
1. The; old; fabulous; Greek
2. The; little; a; affectionate
3. The; weary; the; soft; green
4. The; a; magnificent; vivid
5. Every; good; good; good
6. Every; the; the; famous
7. Fleecy; white
8. every; lofty
9. many; clear; bright
10. a
11. The; beautiful; memorial; the; main; the; city
12. Cautious; dangerous
13. fertile; extensive; valuable; a; great
14. a; massive; a; broad; deep; large; black
15. The; the; a; dreary
16. a; daily
17. The; main; stately
18. a; friendly
19. The; second; the; fourth; broken
20. The; bright; colorful; the; a; wonderful
21. The; old; dusty; the
22. Yellow; green; the; curious
23. The; steaming; blueberry; the
24. An; elegant; the; black
25. the; chirping; baby
26. The; the; first

Lesson 48, Adjectives (P. 68)

B. Discuss your answers with your instructor.
Suggested answers:

1. Puerto Rican
2. Irish
3. South American
4. British
5. French
6. Roman
7. Canadian
8. English
9. Russian

C. Discuss your answers with your instructor.

D. Discuss your answers with your instructor.

Lesson 49, Demonstrative Adjectives (P. 69)

1. those
2. those
3. these
4. those
5. These
6. that
7. this
8. Those
9. those
10. that
11. those
12. these
13. Those
14. Those
15. that
16. these
17. this
18. Those
19. that
20. those
21. this
22. Those
23. these
24. This
25. that

Lesson 50, Comparing with Adjectives (P. 70)

A.
1. gentler; gentlest
2. more helpful; most helpful
3. more difficult; most difficult
4. more troublesome; most troublesome
5. higher; highest
6. more delicious; most delicious
7. more intelligent; most intelligent
8. softer; softest

B.
1. most difficult
2. lovelier
3. more agreeable

Lesson 51, Adverbs (P. 71)

1. rapidly
2. very
3. Slowly; surely
4. Afterward; soundly
5. carefully; thoroughly
6. gracefully
7. Slowly; steadily
8. too; rapidly
9. always; stylishly; neatly
10. quickly; abruptly
11. seriously
12. extremely; slowly; away
13. Always; correctly; clearly
14. rapidly
15. very; quietly
16. patiently; carefully
17. everywhere
18. too; quickly
19. gently
20. here; there; everywhere
21. here; immediately

22. gaily; everywhere
23. Slowly
24. Overhead; brightly
25. thoroughly
26. speedily
27. Carefully
28. quite
29. too

Lesson 52, Comparing with Adverbs (P. 72)

A. 1. faster; fastest
2. more carefully; most carefully
3. more quietly; most quietly
4. slower; slowest
5. more frequently; most frequently
6. more proudly; most proudly
7. more evenly; most evenly
8. longer; longest

B. 1. more seriously   4. worst
2. highest   5. more diligently
3. more thoroughly   6. best

Lesson 53, Using Adjectives and Adverbs (P. 73)

1. carefully	13. surely	25. steadily
2. calm	14. well	26. beautiful
3. furiously	15. easily	27. courteously
4. patiently	16. loudly	28. well
5. cheerfully	17. brightly	29. well
6. well	18. well	30. really
7. promptly	19. quickly	31. foolishly
8. respectfully	20. suddenly	32. foolish
9. happy	21. cautiously	33. loudly
10. legibly	22. accurately	34. rapidly
11. slowly	23. furiously	
12. happily	24. new	

Lesson 54, Prepositions and Prepositional Phrases (P. 74)

The words in bold should be circled.

1. **in** 1847
2. **for** creating the beloved detective Sherlock Holmes
3. **in** the United States; **in** 1884
4. **of** the United States; **in** Kansas
5. **for** miners; **by** Sir Humphrey Davy; **in** 1816
6. **of** North Borneo; **in** houses; **on** stilts; **in** the Brunei River
7. **by** the magician's tricks
8. **in** Canada
9. **in** New York City; **in** 1900
10. **in** the United States; **in** Jamestown; **in** 1619
11. **in** the world; **in** New York; **in** 1832
12. **of** the telephone; **in** Scotland
13. **of** the printing press

14. **of** the giant skyscrapers; **before** us
15. **in** the waves
16. **by** Thomas Jefferson
17. **upon** the quiet valley
18. **to** sleep; **by** the patter; **of** the rain
19. **beneath** the tree
20. **in** the middle; **of** the road
21. **across** the yard; **around** the tree
22. **across** the brook

Lesson 54, Prepositions and Prepositional Phrases (P. 75)

23. **of** our country; **in** 1790
24. **of** violets; **into** perfume
25. **of** a person; **of** blood; **in** one minute
26. **in** 1836
27. **of** the secrets; **of** success; **of** leisure time
28. **at** this hotel
29. **in** Washington, D.C.
30. **of** iron ore; **near** the western end; **of** the Great Lakes
31. **across** this stream; **by** the recent storm
32. **of** cattle; **on** these plains
33. **in** football; **by** a team; **from** Georgia University; **in** 1896
34. **in** Chicago
35. **of** a century ago; **by** stagecoach
36. **of** Delhi; **in** India; **to** the skill; **of** its builders
37. **of** the evening; **by** the rumbling; **of** thunder
38. **in** a tree
39. **on** a sand dune; **in** North Carolina; **in** 1903
40. **in** Richmond; **in** 1885
41. **of** rusty nails; **in** the corner; **of** the garage
42. **near** the edge; **of** that steep cliff
43. **with** a deep snow
44. **in** the accident; **on** the expressway
45. **of** geography; **about** the layout; **of** other lands
46. **of** smoke; **from** the chimney; **of** the cabin
47. **In** the distance; **of** the snow-capped peak
48. **upon** the shelf
49. **At** one time; **of** the United States
50. **between** the goal posts
51. **of** the secretary; **at** the beginning; **of** the meeting
52. **of** cheering fans; **at** the entrance
53. **toward** the ground
54. **beneath** this huge tree
55. **In** the glow; **of** the fading light; **along** the road
56. **near** the new mall
57. **in** the card catalog; **in** the library
58. **through** the halls; **of** the mansion
59. **for** next year

Lesson 55, Conjunctions (P. 76)

1. and
2. whereas
3. since
4. but
5. not only; but also
6. Neither; nor
7. and
8. Neither; nor
9. neither; nor
10. and
11. Either; or
12. and
13. Neither; nor
14. Although
15. when
16. since
17. while
18. Unless; before
19. although
20. Both; and
21. both; and
22. Unless
23. Neither; nor
24. while
25. when
26. Either; or
27. because

Lesson 56, Double Negatives (P. 77)

1. anything
2. anything
3. any
4. anything
5. any
6. any
7. anyone
8. any
9. any
10. any
11. anything
12. anything
13. any
14. any
15. anybody
16. any
17. any
18. anything
19. any
20. any
21. anything
22. any
23. any
24. any
25. any
26. anyone
27. anybody
28. anyone
29. any

Review (P. 78)

A. 1. abstract; Mayor Murayama^P has a great deal of integrity.^C

2. collective; The public^C recognizes Julia's^P singing talent.

3. concrete; Her computer^C is exactly like Craig's.^P

4. abstract; Jim's^P sensitivity^C to others makes him well-liked.

B. 1. women
2. calves
3. porches
4. potatoes
5. sisters-in-law

C. 1. children's
2. lawyers'
3. candidate's
4. men's

D. 1. should have been
2. is designing
3. Did mop
4. might arrive
5. will leave
6. has washed
7. is paying
8. have opened

E. 1. enjoyed; transitive
2. howled; intransitive
3. studied; transitive

Review (P. 79)

F. 1. eaten
2. done
3. came
4. drew
5. spoken

G. 1. imperative
2. indicative
3. subjunctive
4. indicative

H. 1. participle
2. gerund
3. infinitive
4. gerund
5. infinitive

I. 1. possessive
2. object
3. subject
4. object
5. subject

J. The words in bold should be circled.

1. These; **extremely;** hazardous
2. the; long; weary
3. The; large; **soon;** fresh
4. small; the; **quite;** heavy
5. a; graceful; the; **suddenly;** the
6. two; **immediately**

Using What You've Learned (P. 80)

B. Discuss your answers with your instructor.

C. which, Tibet; who, Tibetans; who, herders; that, things

D. Discuss your answers with your instructor.

E. highest

F. Some

G. Discuss your answers with your instructor.

H. to sell; to buy

I. Discuss your answers with your instructor.

Using What You've Learned (P. 81)

K. were

L. Discuss your answers with your instructor.

M. Discuss your answers with your instructor.

N. Discuss your answers with your instructor.

O. Discuss your answers with your instructor.

P. Discuss your answers with your instructor.

Q. Discuss your answers with your instructor.

R. Discuss your answers with your instructor.

Unit 4 — Capitalization and Punctuation

Lesson 57, Using Capital Letters (P. 82)

A. 1. Henry Wadsworth Longfellow wove the history of America into his poems "Evangeline" and "The Courtship of Miles Standish."

2. "The Midnight Ride of Paul Revere" is another of Longfellow's poems.

3. The British ship *Titanic* sank on its first trip from England to the United States.

4. The first law course offered by an American college was taught by George Wythe.

5. He taught many famous people, including Thomas Jefferson and James Monroe.

6. The Mississippi River flows through Vicksburg, Mississippi, and New Orleans, Louisiana.
7. "What time do the church bells ring?" asked Amelia.
8. Robert answered, "I believe they ring every half hour."
9. Many centuries ago, Vikings lived in what is now known as Norway, Sweden, and Denmark.
10. The song "The Battle Hymn of the Republic" was written by Julia Ward Howe.
11. Mr. James Nelson lives in Chicago, Illinois.
12. He asked, "Have you ever seen a waterfall?"
13. The President of the United States lives in the White House.
14. Last summer I visited a Hopi reservation.
15. The Sequoia National Park is on the western slope of the Sierra Nevada Mountains in California.

Lesson 57, Using Capital Letters (P. 83)

B. 1. Mayor Jones and Senator Small attended the awards banquet Friday night.
2. Dr. Fox is a veterinarian at the local animal hospital.
3. The invitation said to respond to Ms. Hilary Johnson.
4. No one expected Judge Randall to rule in favor of the defendant.
5. We were disappointed that Gov. Dickson couldn't speak at graduation.
6. In his place will be Senator Christopher Larson.
7. The speaker will be introduced by Supt. Adams.
8. Will Miss Alden be the new history instructor?
9. Dr. Tabor is a surgeon at Parkside Hospital.
10. His first patient was Mr. William Benton.

C. 1. When is Maj. Hanson expected back from his trip overseas?
2. The garage sale is at 101 W. Charles St.
3. Have you ever been to Orlando, FL?
4. There is a house for sale at the corner of Maple Ave. and Sunset St.
5. Everyone in our company has the first Mon. off in September for Labor Day.
6. The highest award for service was given to Gen. T.J. Quint.
7. The letter from Memphis, TN, took only two days to arrive.
8. Did you know that Col. Kravitz will be stationed in Dover, NH?
9. His address will be 1611 Falmouth Harbor, Dover, NH 03805.

Lesson 58, Using End Punctuation (P. 84)

A. 1. ?   4. .   7. .   10. ?   13. .
   2. .   5. .   8. .   11. ?   14. ?
   3. ?   6. ?   9. ?   12. .

B. Have you ever heard of Harriet Tubman and the Underground Railroad? During the Civil War in the United States, Harriet Tubman, a former slave, helped more than three hundred slaves escape to freedom. Tubman led slaves on the dangerous route of the Underground Railroad. It was not actually a railroad but a series of secret homes and shelters that led through the South to the free North and Canada. How dangerous was her work? There were large rewards offered by slaveholders for her capture. But Tubman was never caught. She said proudly, "I never lost a passenger." She was called the Moses of her people.

During the war, she worked as a spy for the Union army. An excellent guide, she would lead soldiers into enemy camps. She also served as a nurse and cook for the soldiers. She was well respected among leading abolitionists of the time. She was also a strong supporter of women's rights.

Do you know what she did after the war? She settled in Auburn, New York, and took care of her parents and any other needy black person. She was always low on money but never refused anyone. Later, she set up a home for poor African Americans.

Lesson 58, Using End Punctuation (P. 85)

C. 1. . or !   6. .   11. !
   2. !   7. !; ! or .   12. !; !
   3. .   8. !   13. !
   4. !; ! or .   9. .   14. .
   5. .   10. .   15. .

D. Use of exclamation points and periods may vary. Sample paragraphs shown below:

Which animal do you think has been on Earth longer, the dog or the cat? If you answered the cat, you're right! About 5,000 years ago in Egypt, cats became accepted household pets. That was a long time ago! Cats were actually worshipped in ancient Egypt.

The different members of the cat family have certain things in common. House cats and wild cats all walk on the tips of their toes. Isn't that incredible? Even though all cats don't like water, they can all swim. Another thing that all cats have in common is a keen hunting ability. Part of this is due to their eyesight. They see well at night and in dim light. Did you know that the cat is the only animal that purrs? A cat uses its whiskers to feel. Its sense of touch is located in its whiskers. The coat of a cat can be long-haired or short-haired, solid-colored or striped. Some cats even have spots! Can you name any types of cats?

Lesson 59, Using Commas (P. 86)

A. 1. Anita, Travis, and José went to the tennis tournament.
2. Before they found their seats, the first match had already begun.
3. It was a close game, and they weren't disappointed by the final score.
4. They had come to cheer for Antonio Fergas, and he was the winner.
5. Although his opponent was very good, Fergas never missed returning a serve.
6. While they watched the match, Anita clapped, cheered, and kept score.
7. Travis and José watched a number of different matches, but Anita followed Fergas.
8. He was signing autographs, and Anita was first in line.
9. Antonio asked her name, signed a tennis ball, and shook her hand.
10. Because they enjoyed the match so much, Travis, José, and Anita made plans to come back for the final match the next day.
11. They planned to see the men's, women's and doubles' finals.
12. Fergas won the entire tournament, and he became the youngest champion in the history of the tournament.

B. 1. "The first match starts at 9:00 A.M.," said Travis.
2. Anita asked, "Do you want to get seats in the same section as yesterday?"
3. "That's fine with me," said José.
4. José said, "Fergas's first match is in Court B."
5. "I'll bring the binoculars," said Anita, "and you can bring the cooler."

Lesson 59, Using Commas (P. 87)

C. 1. Dr. Perillo, a nutritionist, is an expert on proper eating.
2. "Students, it's important to eat a well-balanced diet," she said.
3. "Yes, but how do we know what the right foods are?" asked one student.
4. "First, you need to look carefully at your eating habits," said Dr. Perillo.
5. "Yes, you will keep a journal of the foods you eat," she said.
6. "Dr. Perillo, what do you mean by the right servings?" asked Emilio.
7. "Okay, good question," she said.
8. "A serving, Emilio, is a certain amount of a food," said Dr. Perillo.
9. "Dave, a cross-country runner, will need more calories than a less active student," explained Dr. Perillo.
10. "Class, remember to eat foods from the five basic food groups," she said.

D. Our neighbor, Patrick, has fruit trees on his property. "Patrick, what kinds of fruit do you grow?" I asked. "Well, I grow peaches, apricots, pears, and plums," he replied. "Wow! That's quite a variety," I said. Patrick's son, Jonathan, helps his dad care for the trees. "Oh, it's constant work and care," Jonathan said, "but the delicious results are worth the effort." After harvesting the fruit, Jonathan's grandmother, Allison, cans the fruit for use throughout the year. She makes preserves, and she gives them as gifts for special occasions. Allison sells some of her preserves to Chris Simon, the owner of a local shop. People come from all over the county to buy Allison's preserves.

Jonathan's aunt, Christina, grows corn, tomatoes, beans, and squash in her garden. Each year she selects her best vegetables and enters them in the fair. She has won blue ribbons, medals, and certificates for her vegetables. "Oh, I just like being outside. That's why I enjoy gardening," Christina said. Christina's specialty, squash-and-tomato bread, is one of the most delicious breads I have ever tasted.

Lesson 60, Using Quotation Marks and Apostrophes (P. 88)

A. 1. "Mary, do you think this is Christine's pen?" asked Heather.
2. Heather said, "I don't know. It looks like the kind she uses."
3. "Well, I think it's out of ink," Mary replied.
4. "Have you seen Barbara's car?" asked Sandy.
5. "No," said Beth, "I haven't gotten over to her apartment this week."
6. Sandy said, "It sure is pretty. I can't wait to ride in it."
7. "I can't believe how late it is!" exclaimed Alan.
8. Paul asked, "Where are you going on vacation this summer?"
9. "My brother and I are visiting our parents in Maine," said Peter.
10. "Tell me," Alison said, "how many cats do you have?"
11. Alison said, "The last time we counted, there were four."
12. "Will you be taking the bus home," asked James, "or do you need a ride?"

B. 1. I'm; can't
2. can't; Beth's
3. I'll; nights'
4. I've; bandleader's
5. isn't; Porter's

Lesson 61, Using Colons and Semicolons (P. 89)

A. 1. At 9:10 this morning, we'll be leaving for the natural history museum.
2. Please bring the following materials with you: pencils, paper, erasers, and a notebook.
3. The bus will be back at 4:00 to pick us up.
4. The special exhibit on birds contains the following types: prehistoric birds, sea birds, and domestic birds.
5. The letter we wrote to the museum began: "Dear Sir: Please let us know when the special exhibition on penguins will be shown at your museum."
6. He told us that we could find out more about the following kinds of penguins: the Emperor, the Adélie, and the Magellan.
7. We were afraid there would be so much to see that we wouldn't be ready to leave at 3:30 when the museum closed.

B. 1. Colleen is a clever teacher; she is also an inspiring one.
2. Her lectures are interesting; they are full of information.
3. She has a college degree in history; world history is her specialty.
4. She begins her classes by answering questions; she ends them by asking questions.

Lesson 62, Using Other Punctuation (P. 90)

A. 1. The director told us that there would be room for only two busloads, or eighty-four people.
2. The play was going to be in an old-fashioned theater.
3. Between acts the theater was completely dark, but the orchestra con-tinued to play anyway.
4. The theater was so small that there were seats for only ninety-two people.
5. The vice-president was played by Alan Lowe.

B. 1. There was a loud boom—what a fright—from the back of the theater.
2. We all turned around—I even jumped up—to see what it was.
3. It was part of the play—imagine that—meant to add suspense.
4. I'd love to see the play again—maybe next week—and bring Andrea.

C. 1. We saw the movie Of Mice and Men after we had read the novel.
2. In Spanish, Hasta la vista means "See you later."
3. My favorite book is Little Women.
4. I took a copy of Life magazine out of the library.

Review (P. 91)

A. 1. Last Thanksgiving we spent the holiday at my aunt's house in Florida.
2. It was wonderful to be warm in November!
3. We visited the Riverdale Gardens, Sea World, and the Ringling Museum.
4. One day, we went to see the ship Ocean Dream.
5. The boat's captain, Mr. Harvey Land, took us on a tour.

6. He asked if any of us had been to Crystal Island.
7. When we answered no, he said he'd take us there on Friday.
8. After that journey, I read Seafaring Around the World.

B. 1. "We saw twenty-four kinds of fish off the coast of Florida," said Paul.
2. "Did you snorkel," asked Marie, "or did you stay on the ship?"
3. Paul answered, "We began to snorkel in the shallow water at 2:00."
4. The captain's first mate, Jake, is an experienced diver.
5. "He offered to give us lessons," said Paul.
6. "What would he teach you?" asked Andrew.
7. "He'd teach us," said Paul, "how to approach the fish without scaring them away."
8. "That must be great!" exclaimed Marie.
9. "Yes, I can't wait to learn," said Paul.
10. Paul said, "I think he'd be a fine teacher. I know he's a great swimmer."

C.
1200 S. Clarke St.
Chicago, IL 60202
June 10, 2006

Dear Mr. Anderson,
  I can't tell you how much we appreciated the time you spent with us in Florida. It was the greatest trip ever! Because of our trip, my sister and I plan to take Introduction to Oceanography at the Seaworld Institute here in Chicago. The course is offered to people of all ages at the Alcott Aquarium. Don't you think it's funny that Chicago has the Seaworld Institute, and we aren't even near the ocean? The closest thing we have is Lake Michigan. Thanks again for all your help and time.
Sincerely,
Paul Mendoza

Review (P. 92)

D.
1907 E. Adams Blvd.
Phoenix, AZ 94733
Aug. 18, 2006

Dear KMOL Radio:
  I listened with interest to Peter Katz and Filipa Guerra on your 10:00 show "Talk About Town" last Friday night. Though I tried to call in, the lines were always busy. I thought I'd try writing; it will at least make me feel better.
  I really couldn't believe my own ears! What in the world do those two have in common with the public in general? Mr. Katz said he'd never had to work a day in his life. Ms. Guerra said she'd never been out of the state of New Mexico. Well, most of the people in Arizona have to work. Many have come from another state. Neither of them has the right to tell working-class people how to live. My suggestions are these: take a survey, show it to your guests, and demand an on-air apology from them.
  By the way, I have long wondered what KMOL—your call letters—stand for, if anything. Would you

164

Answer Key

please answer that sometime on the air? Thanks for your time.

Yours truly,
Erica Mallett

Using What You've Learned (P. 93)

A. Have you ever heard the story called "The Dog and His Bone"? There once was a dog that had a new bone. "This is a great bone," said the dog to himself. The dog decided to take a walk and carried the bone proudly in its mouth. He went down a dirt road and over a bridge. As he was crossing the bridge, he looked down into the river. "Wow!" said the dog. "Look at that big bone in the water." The dog thought to himself, "I'd rather have that bone than the one I have right now." Can you guess what happened next? Well, the dog opened his mouth and dropped the bone—a foolish thing to do—into the river. When the splash of the bone hitting the water stopped, the dog looked for the bigger bone. However, he didn't see it anymore. What he did see was his old bone sinking to the bottom of the river.

There is an incredible man, Scott Targot, who lives in my town. His nickname is the Ironman. People call him Ironman Targot because he has won several triathlons. Do you know what a triathlon is? Some people consider it the ultimate sports contest. Athletes have to swim for 2.4 miles, ride a bike for 112 miles, and run for 26.2 miles. Just one of those alone is a lot of work. Scott will train from February to August in preparation for a triathlon in Hawaii. Scott says, "I wouldn't want to be doing anything else with my time." Each day during training he gets up at 7:00, loosens up for a half-hour, then runs from 7:30 to 8:30. After he cools down a little, he takes a 20-mile bike ride. At the end of the ride, he swims for an hour and a half. "Yes, I get tired," he says, "but I usually feel refreshed after swimming." Last, he lifts light weights and takes a break to do some reading. His favorite book is *You Can Do It.*

A triathlon is supposed to be completed in less than seventeen hours. The record is less than half that time. "That's my goal," says Scott. He's still trying to break 14 hours and ten minutes. Scott's usually one of the top finishers.

Using What You've Learned (P. 94)

B. Discuss your answers with your instructor.

C. Discuss your answers with your instructor.

 Unit 5 Composition

Lesson 63, Writing Sentences (P. 95)

A. Discuss your answers with your instructor.

B. Discuss your answers with your instructor.

Lesson 64, Writing Paragraphs (P. 96)

A. The following sentences should be crossed out. Discuss your answers with your instructor.
1. Bob's dad is an experienced carpenter.
2. Sometimes she got jobs baby-sitting for families with children in the swimming program.

B. Discuss your answers with your instructor.

Lesson 65, Writing Topic Sentences (P. 97)

A. 1. Working in a fast-food restaurant is a good first job for young people.
2. A popular ice cream parlor in our town hires young people.
3. Computers are used in fast-food restaurants.

B. Discuss your answers with your instructor.

C. Discuss your answers with your instructor.

Lesson 66, Writing Supporting Details (P. 98)

A. Topic sentence:

In almost every professional sport, there are far more applicants than available jobs.

Supporting Details:
1. …several hundred players are selected…
2. …only about ten percent are actually signed…
3. …this number shrinks each year…
4. …team owners want smaller and smaller teams.

B. 1. Discuss your answers with your instructor.
2. …team owners want smaller and smaller teams.

C. Discuss your answers with your instructor.

Lesson 67, Topic and Audience (P. 99)

A. 1. d   2. b   3. c   4. a

B. 1. The evening was full of surprises.
2. Discuss your answers with your instructor.
3. Discuss your answers with your instructor.

C. Discuss your answers with your instructor.

Lesson 68, Brainstorming (P. 100)

A. Discuss your answers with your instructor.

B. Discuss your answers with your instructor.

C. Discuss your answers with your instructor.

Lesson 69, Outlining (P. 101)

Discuss your answers with your instructor.

Lesson 70, Persuasive Composition (P. 102)

B. Discuss your answers with your instructor.

Lesson 70, Persuasive Composition (P. 103)

C. Discuss your answers with your instructor.

D. Discuss your answers with your instructor.

E. Discuss your answers with your instructor.

Lesson 71, Revising and Proofreading (P. 104)

A. Personal safety is one of the most important social issues today. Adults and children are worried about staying safe in all these places: their homes, their schools, and the places they go to have fun. One of the best things a person can do is to act with confidence and awareness. Confidence means "believing," and awareness means "seeing." Several studies have shown that people who act with confidence and awareness do not look like easy targets, which is what criminals look for.

Lesson 71, Revising and Proofreading (P. 105)

B. Proofreading and revision may vary. Samples are shown below.

¶ When your outside your home, your body language is important very. If you straigt stand, walk purposefully, and pay attention to what is around you, you will discourage Criminals because you appear strong and alert. along with confidence and awareness, Another tool you can use all the time is your voice, you can yell. Crimnals dont like to draw to attention themselves, and they don't like to be seen. Yelling may sometimes be embarrassing, but your safety is more important than worrying about imbarassment.

¶ at home, its important to always keep your doors and windows locked, you should never open the door to someone you don't know. You don't have to be polite to somebody who may be trying to do you harm. This also applys to the telephone. If sombody you don't know calls and tries to keep you engaged in conservation, just hang up. you don't have to be polite to somebody who is intruding in your life, especially if you don't know the person. always keep your safety in mind and act in a way that discourages criminals from bothering you.

When you're outside your home, your body language is very important. If you stand straight, walk purposefully, and pay attention to what is around you, you will discourage criminals because you appear strong and alert. Along with confidence and awareness, another tool you can use all the time is your voice—you can yell. Criminals don't like to draw attention to themselves, and they don't like to be seen. Yelling may sometimes be embarrassing, but your safety is more important than worrying about embarrassment.

At home, it's important to always keep your doors and windows locked. You should never open the door to someone you don't know. You don't have to be polite to somebody who may be trying to do you harm. This also applies to the telephone. If somebody you don't know calls and tries to keep you engaged in a conversation, just hang up. You don't have to be polite to somebody who is intruding in your life, especially if you don't know the person. Always keep your safety in mind and act in a way that discourages criminals from bothering you.

Review (P. 106)

A. Discuss your answers with your instructor.
B. Discuss your answers with your instructor.
C. The following sentences should be underlined and labeled as follows:
   sentence 2: example
   sentence 3: reason
   sentence 4: fact

Review (P. 107)

D. Suggested outline form:
   Topic: Pruning trees takes great skill.
   I. Pruning the tree
      A. Climb the tree
      B. Brace your body firmly
      C. Choose and trim bad wood
   II. Cleaning up
      A. Rake tree trash
      B. Haul trash
E. Answers will vary.
F. Proofreading and revision may vary. Samples are shown below.

¶ Artists choose from his materials that already are in existents to create their works of art, all materials have there own qualities. artists must know the characteristicks of their chosen materyal. They must work with it and not aginst it, materials are shaped in many ways, cutting, melting, hammering, and wearving are some of those waze.

Artists choose from materials that are already in existence to create their works of art. All materials have their own qualities. Artists must know the characteristics of their chosen material. They must work with it and not against it. Materials are shaped in many ways. Cutting, melting, hammering, and weaving are some of those ways.

Using What You've Learned (P. 108)

A. Discuss your answers with your instructor.

B. Discuss your answers with your instructor.

C. Discuss your answers with your instructor.

Using What You've Learned (P. 109)

D. Discuss your answers with your instructor.

E. Discuss your answers with your instructor.

F. Discuss your answers with your instructor.

 Unit 6 Study Skills

Lesson 72, Dictionary: Syllables (P. 110)

A.
1. rum-mage
2. nev-er-the-less
3. a-bom-i-na-ble
4. sil-hou-ette
5. bi-o-log-i-cal
6. sta-tion-er-y
7. cor-re-spon-dence
8. char-ac-ter
9. en-thu-si-asm
10. a-ban-don
11. treach-er-ous
12. ef-fort-less
13. ro-man-tic
14. nau-ti-cal
15. ac-cel-er-ate
16. fi-nan-cial
17. sig-nif-i-cance
18. un-im-por-tant
19. com-mer-cial
20. bal-le-ri-na

B.
1. imag-ination; imagina-tion
2. Discuss your answers with your instructor.
3. trop-ical; tropi-cal
4. Discuss your answers with your instructor.
5. Discuss your answers with your instructor.
6. Discuss your answers with your instructor.
7. Discuss your answers with your instructor.
8. ef-ficient; effi-cient
9. clean-liness; cleanli-ness

Lesson 73, Dictionary: Pronunciation (P. 111)

A. 1. me   2. 5   3. zh   4. o   5. ä

B.
1. own
2. heat
3. rod
4. talk
5. speed
6. water
7. wait
8. spell
9. angel
10. must
11. fear
12. hard
13. fright
14. soon

Lesson 74, Dictionary: Definitions and Parts of Speech (P. 112)

1. portion
2. popular
3. noun
4. 1; 4; 2
5. pleasing to many people
6. Discuss your answers with your instructor.
7. Discuss your answers with your instructor.
8. Discuss your answers with your instructor.

Lesson 75, Dictionary: Etymologies (P. 113)

1. punk
2. Old French; Latin
3. punk
4. pueblo
5. novel; pueblo
6. new things
7. pueblo
8. Latin
9. punk; reef
10. pueblo
11. reef

Lesson 76, Using Parts of a Book (P. 114)

A.
1. *Language Exercises*
2. Harcourt Achieve Inc.
3. 110
4. inside back cover
5. 2006
6. 3, 101, 107, 109, 140, 146
7. 82
8. 46–50
9. Concrete, Abstract, and Collective Nouns
10. 39, 40, 78, 88, 136–137
11. 55
12. 13
13. 18

B.
1. title page
2. table of contents
3. copyright page
4. index

Lesson 77, Using Visual Aids (P. 115)

A. 1. Karen; Carlos   3. May   5. graph
2. May and June   4. chart

Lesson 77, Using Visual Aids (P. 116)

B.
1. west
2. Preston Road
3. about 2 miles
4. Interstate
5. yes
6. east/west
7. two
8. about $8\frac{1}{2}$ to 9 miles

Lesson 78, Using the Library (P. 117)

A.
1. 900–999
2. 600–699
3. 400–499
4. 500–599
5. 100–199
6. 000–099
7. 700–799
8. 800–899
9. 500–599
10. 300–399
11. 800–899
12. 200–299
13. 900–999
14. 000–099
15. 500–599

B. Discuss your answers with your instructor.

Lesson 79, Using the Card Catalog (P. 118)

A. 1. Robert Leventhal
  2. no
  3. 331.20 Le
  4. 1993
  5. Answers may vary. Suggested: whales
  6. A great place to visit

B. 1. subject   **3.** title   **5.** author
  2. author   **4.** subject   **6.** title

Lesson 80, Using an Encyclopedia (P. 119)

A. 1. Discuss your answers with your instructor.
  2. 1832–1888
  3. Germantown, PA
  4. Discuss your answers with your instructor.
  5. She was a nurse.

B. 1. Discuss your answers with your instructor.
  2. bracelet or necklace
  3. the Medic Alert Foundation International
  4. Answers may vary. Suggested: medical information
  5. the foundation's

C. Discuss your answers with your instructor.

Lesson 81, Using an Encyclopedia Index (P. 120)

1. 1
2. 79, 389
3. yes
4. alligator
5. crocodile, reptile
6. animal
7. alligator and crocodile
8. 11
9. dingo
10. mountain lion, cougar
11. crocodile
12. c

Lesson 82, Using a Thesaurus (P. 121)

A. 1. move
  2. turn, budge, shift, retrieve, carry, transport, retreat, crawl, arouse, progress
  3. arouse
  4. turn
  5. stay, stop, stabilize
  6. stay

B. 1. carry   **5.** turn
  2. retrieve   **6.** crawl
  3. transport   **7.** progress
  4. shift   **8.** budge

Lesson 83, Using the *Readers' Guide* (P. 122)

1. P. Dwyer
2. Jean Cretien
3. *Business Week*
4. shopping
5. 106
6. November 1993
7. both
8. October 1993
9. 30 – 31
10. 58 – 59

Lesson 84, Using an Atlas (P. 123)

A. 1. Central America   **4.** Pan-American Highway
  2. 7   **5.** Belize
  3. Volcán Tajumulco   **6.** Managua

B. 1. an industry map
  2. where the most mountains are
  3. a climate map

Lesson 85, Using an Almanac (P. 124)

1. vacation
2. shopping/business
3. shopping/business, work, and other
4. circle graph
5. school/church
6. social
7. 34
8. 5 miles
9. 114 miles
10. social

Lesson 86, Choosing Reference Sources (P. 125)

1. atlas or encyclopedia
2. dictionary
3. encyclopedia or *Readers' Guide*
4. dictionary
5. thesaurus
6. *Readers' Guide*
7. dictionary
8. atlas
9. encyclopedia
10. thesaurus
11. encyclopedia or *Readers' Guide*
12. dictionary
13. *Readers' Guide*
14. encyclopedia
15. almanac
16. atlas or encyclopedia
17. thesaurus

Lesson 87, Using Reference Sources (P. 126)

A. Discuss your answers with your instructor.

B. Discuss your answers with your instructor.

Lesson 87, Using Reference Sources (P. 127)

C. Discuss your answers with your instructor.

Review (P. 128)

A. 1. 2; 2; 3   **6.** Sentences will vary.
  2. denim   **7.** diet
  3. noun; noun   **8.** Old French and Latin
  4. Old French and Greek   **9.** desert; diet
  5. a. desert   **10.** December
    b. December

B. 1. table of contents
2. index
3. copyright page
4. title page
5. copyright page
6. table of contents
7. table of contents
8. copyright page

Review (P. 129)

C. 1. Ellis   2. Linn   3. Sharon

D. 1. almanac
2. card catalog
3. encyclopedia
4. thesaurus
5. *Readers' Guide*
6. atlas
7. card catalog
8. dictionary
9. encyclopedia
10. atlas

Using What You've Learned (P. 130)

A. 1. Discuss your answers with your instructor.
2. con-di-tion
3. noun; verb
4. Discuss your answers with your instructor.

B. 1. author card
2. Writing Effective Speeches
3. Henry Ehrlich
4. no

C. 1. Discuss your answers with your instructor.
2. Yes, the kernels are sometimes edible.
3. 30 feet

D. 1. Leslie Ann Kerns
2. The Trouble with Money
3. *Time*
4. no

Using What You've Learned (P. 131)

E. Discuss your answers with your instructor.
1. 30; 15
2. November and March
3. May; January
4. no

F. Answers may vary. Suggested:
1. west
2. salt
3. corn
4. fish, seafood

Final Reviews

Final Review, Unit 1 (P. 132)

1. H	4. H	7. A	10. H	13. S	16. S
2. A	5. A	8. H	11. S	14. S	17. A
3. S	6. S	9. S	12. H	15. H	18. H

1. alight
2. down
3. arm
4. pad
5. racket
6. tear
7. mine
8. fan

1. P; C	4. P; P	7. P; S	10. S; S
2. S; S	5. P; C	8. S; C	
3. C; P	6. S; C	9. P; C	

Final Review, Unit 1 (P. 133)

1. I've	7. he'd	13. they'll
2. we'll	8. I'm	14. we'd
3. they're	9. that's	15. doesn't
4. couldn't	10. didn't	16. it's
5. you've	11. won't	17. wouldn't
6. don't	12. there's	18. I'll

1. +	5. −	9. +	13. +
2. I	6. I	10. N	14. −
3. −	7. +	11. I	15. I
4. −	8. I	12. +	16. N

1. stay hopeful
2. makes one mad
3. stay up late
4. did not finish
5. change
6. find
7. have enough money
8. give up
9. admit being wrong
10. tell a secret

Final Review, Unit 2 (P. 134)

1. D; . or E; !	4. E; !	7. E; !	10. IN; ?
2. IM; .	5. IN; ?	8. D; .	
3. IN; ?	6. IN; ?	9. IM; .	

1. typed and proofread
2. me
3. report
4. "A"
5. that Ellen wrote
6. read the book two times
7. Everyone in the class
8. were completed
9. The reports had to be in on time; they would lose a grade
10. before the due date

1. who defended the criminal; adjective
2. before we knew it; adverb
3. that Edward had been to Niagara Falls; adjective
4. Although it was still early; adverb
5. that people like to visit; adjective
6. When Rebecca heard that; adverb
7. because it had never been saddled before; adverb
8. since the crime rate began to rise; adverb
9. whose last names begin with "M"; adjective
10. After the way Joe acted; adverb

Final Review, Unit 2 (P. 135)

1.–10. Discuss your answers with your instructor.

1.–8. Discuss your answers with your instructor.

Suggested:

1. It was the middle of the night. The smoke alarm went off, and we woke up frightened.
2. The reason we called you here is clear. We need to make some decisions today.

Discuss your answers with your instructor.

Final Review, Unit 3 (P. 136)

Answers will vary. Sample paragraphs follow:

The art of growing and raising miniature trees is called Bonsai. The Japanese word bonsai means "tray-planted." The Chinese first grew bonsai over 1,000 years ago. Growing bonsai became increasingly popular in Japan during the 1800s. It has been a hobby in the United States since the early 1900s and is still growing in popularity.

Bonsai trees are normal trees that are made into miniatures. They can be made from many types of trees, including evergreens, pines, flowers, and fruit trees. It takes much skill, time, and patience to make the bonsai tree look like a miniature replica of a tree in nature. Gardeners must practice for years to learn how to make bonsai. The bonsai branches are pruned and wired to create desired shapes. The dwarfed roots are kept in small containers and also pruned to stunt their growth.

A bonsai tree ranges in height from two inches to two or three feet. Would you have guessed that a smaller tree takes much longer (sometimes ten years) to achieve its ideal shape and size? It can grow inside or outside. In Japan, the healthiest and largest bonsai are kept outside and are only brought inside for viewing. Some live for 100 years or more. In Japan, many Japanese families pass them down to the next generation as a treasured heirloom.

Final Review, Unit 3 (P. 137)

1. concrete; $\overset{P}{\underline{\text{Niagara Falls}}}$ is on the $\overset{C}{\underline{\text{border}}}$ between the $\overset{P}{\underline{\text{United States}}}$ and $\overset{P}{\underline{\text{Canada}}}$.

2. collective; The $\overset{C}{\underline{\text{citizens}}}$ voted overwhelmingly for $\overset{P}{\underline{\text{Judge Harriman}}}$.

3. abstract; $\overset{P}{\underline{\text{Daniel}}}$ showed his $\overset{C}{\underline{\text{courage}}}$ by diving into $\overset{P}{\underline{\text{Lake Michigan}}}$.

1. volcanoes   3. benches   5. women
2. paintings   4. deer   6. mothers-in-law

1. authors'   3. highway's 5. envelope's
2. men's   4. sky's   6. Donna's

1. shown   2. took   3. done   4. spoke

1. possessive   3. subject
2. demonstrative

1. well   2. quickly   3. happiest

The words in bold should be circled.

1. **in** the red house; **on** the left side; **of** the street
2. **to** the windows; **into** the building

Final Review, Unit 4 (P. 138)

The first letter in each of the following words should be circled and capitalized, and end punctuation should be added as shown:

1. Our; June; .
2. Will; Mrs.; Hernandez; Dr.; Altman; ?
3. A; Charlie's; Place; Italian; .
4. My; Saturday; Sunday; Clark; St.; Prairie; Lane; .
5. Mr.; Johnson; Bikes; You; .
6. Will; Country; Kitchen; Oakland; Ave.; ?
7. Last; Mark; Gable; Rosemont; I'm; !
8. Dancers; Phillips; School; Robert; Louis; Stevenson's; Treasure; Island; .
9. The; Maple; Crane; Saturday; .
10. There; Carlyle; Rosemont; Meadow Grove; Newton; .

1. "Why are you telling me all this now?" asked Cynthia.
2. You can use books, encyclopedias, and atlases when doing research.
3. "I've spent the last two hours waiting," said Mary.
4. Scott said, "You'll be much happier when you get settled."
5. Lloyd, Jane, and Debra are all going in the same car.
6. "Won't you please help me with this?" asked Joe.
7. "She's the one," said Ellen, "who brought that wonderful dessert."
8. Nissans, Hondas, and Toyotas are Japanese vehicles.
9. "My fruit salad recipe," she said, "calls for oranges, apples, bananas, and raisins."
10. Karen mowed the yard, weeded the garden, and watered the flowers.
11. Sara's car was in the shop for two weeks.
12. Janet, Rosa, and Alicia went to Diane's dinner party.

1230 E. Clark St.
San Diego, CA 94024

Mr. Charles Martinelli
3340 W. Belden Street
San Diego, CA 94022

Dear Mr. Martinelli:

On June 10 and 11, our neighborhood will be holding its fifth-anniversary Summer Block Party. It is a day-long event with contests, performances, great food, and sidewalk sales. In past years, local restaurants and businesses have donated food and prizes. We hope your restaurant, Charlie's Place, will join in and help make our block party a success. I remember you once saying, "I'd love to pitch in next time." Please call us at 555-1270, and let us know if you want to contribute this year. We look forward to hearing from you soon.

Sincerely,
Angela Hernandez

Final Review, Unit 4 (P. 139)

1. You mean that you said—and I'm quoting you now—that he was "too big for his britches"?
2. I read Lonesome Dove three times; it was such a wonderful book.
3. I addressed my greeting "Dear Madam or Sir:" since I didn't know whether the owner was a man or a woman.
4. The festival Saturday runs from 10:00 A.M. to 5:00 P.M.
5. Tony bought a blue-green convertible when he got his new job.
6. My sister-in-law writes children's stories; they are also fun for adults to read.
7. My favorite show is on every Tuesday at 8:00; it's the best show on television.
8. The local play had parts for seventy-eight people; men, women, and children were invited to audition.
9. I use the money from my part-time job to pay for these hobbies: photography, dancing, and horseback riding.
10. Connie has seen her favorite movie, Gone With the Wind, twenty-two times.

Final Review, Unit 5 (P. 140)

1.–3. Discuss your answers with your instructor.
Discuss your answers with your instructor.
1. X   **3.** X   **4.** X
Suggested outline:
Topic: Painting Is Hard Work

I. Preparing the surface
   A. Scrape off the old paint
   B. Sand the surface until smooth

II. Painting
   A. Stir the paint thoroughly
   B. Spread the paint with even strokes

Final Review, Unit 5 (P. 141)

Discuss your answers with your instructor. Samples are shown below.

¶most people do not know that there are 48 types of eagles in the world people immediately think of golden eagles and bald eagles, two kinds that breed in North america, what most eagles halve in common are large, powerful wings and a sharp beak most eagles return the to same nest each year and keep the same mates for life. unfortunately, both bald and golden eagles our declining in population due to extensive hunting by man and loss of they're natural environment. laws now Protect the eagles.¶ many types of eagles are the size of hawks. but the large bald eagle and the golden eagle, with wing spans of about seven feet and body sizes from 30 to 35 inches, are smaller than the harpy eagle of central and South America. The harpy eagles range from 30 to 37 inches and live in jungles.

Discuss your answers with your instructor.

Final Review, Unit 6 (P. 142)

1. c
2. 3; 5
3. Discuss your answers with your instructor.
4. Discuss your answers with your instructor.
5. noun
6. 2; 1
7. koun′tē; märk
8. mark
9. county
10. mark

1. dictionary	5. *Readers' Guide*
2. encyclopedia	6. almanac
3. thesaurus	7. dictionary
4. atlas or encyclopedia	8. encyclopedia

Final Review, Unit 6 (P. 143)

1. go to the theater	3. chart
2. April and May	4. graph

1. iron	3. Bowie
2. $2,000,000	4. Bowie

Check What You've Learned (P. 144)

A. 1. S   2. A   3. H   4. H

B. 1. account

C. 1. S   2. P   3. C   4. P

D. 1. she would   2. did not

E. boring

F. 1. b

G. The words in bold should be circled.

   1. IM; (You), **take**   3. E; I, **won**
   2. IN; Who, **ate**   4. D; I, **forgot**

H. 1. CP   2. CS

I. 1. CS   2. RO   3. I

J. [After he had returned,] Enrique told Armando the
    DO
   truth.

Check What You've Learned (P. 145)

K. The words in bold should be circled.

Before **Edward** could stop his car, **Mr. Huang**
opened the door and jumped out.

L. The words in bold should be circled.

Our local newspaper, *The Hunterstown Gazette*,
is the oldest in the state.

M. 1. past   3. future
   2. present   4. past

N. 1. began, ate   3. took, chose
   2. Teaching, been   4. set, lay

O. 1 should be circled.

P. The words in bold should be circled.

   1. SP; **We**   3. PP; **their**
   2. OP; **her**   4. IP; **Someone**

Q. The word in bold should be circled.

Annette served the wonderful dinner with her
customary flair.

R. 1. adjective   3. adjective   5. adjective
   2. adverb   4. adverb   6. adverb

S. The words in bold should be circled.

Hoan pretended to be asleep when his father
came **into** his room to wake him **for** breakfast.

Check What You've Learned (P. 146)

T.
                    408 Greene St.
                    Centerville, OH 56109
                    March 15, 2006

Dear Charles,

   I can't wait until next month! It's going to be so
much fun to finally meet you after all these years of
writing. I know it's still winter in Moscow, but when
you get here, it'll be springtime.

   Here's what you should bring: jeans, shirts,
shorts, tennis shoes, and one dressy outfit. I've got
your schedule memorized and will be waiting at the
gate at exactly 11:23. Are you ready for the time of
your life? I hope so!

                    Your friend,
                    Sheila

U. 1. 2   2. 3   3. 4   4. 1

V. 1. brainstorming   3. persuading
   2. outlining

Check What You've Learned (P. 147)

W. Judge Mayers sentenced the defendant to ten
years in prison.

X. 1. noun   3. so-ci-e-ty
   2. before   4. soak / sock

Y. 1. h   3. c   5. f   7. b
   2. d   4. e   6. g   8. a